March of America Facsimile Series

Number 2

Cosmographiae Introductio

Martin Waldseemüller

Cosmographiae Introductio

by Martin Waldseemüller
and the English translation of Joseph Fischer
and Franz von Wieser

ANN ARBOR

UNIVERSITY MICROFILMS, INC.

A Subsidiary of Xerox Corporation

REPRINTED FROM

U.S. CATHOLIC HISTORICAL SOCIETY

MONOGRAPH IV

BY PERMISSION OF THE SOCIETY

Foreword

Introduction To Cosmography...To Which Are Added The Four Voyages Of Amerigo Vespucci was first printed in 1507. The author, the German geographer Martin Waldsee-müller, intended the book to accompany and to explain a globe and a plane projection map of the world which he also prepared at the same time. Waldseemüller's book is probably best known for having given the New World its name, "America." However, of more practical worth, Waldseemül-ler revealed that on the basis of information supplied by the voyages of Amerigo Vespucci it was evident that the lands to the west formed part of a previously unknown continent. This meant that an ocean must lie on the other side, separat-ing the newly discovered continent from Asia. These find-ings dampened some of the enthusiasm which Columbus had aroused with his announcement of the discovery of a direct route to the Orient.

Waldseemüller announced at the beginning of his book that "no one can obtain a thorough knowledge of Cosmog-raphy without some previous understanding of astronomy, nor even of astronomy itself without the principles of geom-etry." For this reason, Waldseemüller used the opening chap-ters to familiarize his readers with the basic elements of these sciences before he settled down to a discussion of world geography. Waldseemüller acknowledged his great debt to previous geographers and mentioned Ptolemy with special respect. Yet he had not always followed Ptolemy, "partic-ularly as regards the new lands," he explained, because he thought it profitable "to pay more attention to the informa-tion gathered in our own times." In discussing the divisions of the world, Waldseemüller made his celebrated statement that "a fourth part has been discovered by Amerigo Vespucci ... I see no reason why anyone should justly object to calling this part Amerige, i.e., the land of Amerigo, or America, after Amerigo, its discoverer." A better acquaintance with the discoveries of Columbus evidently led Waldseemüller to omit use of the term on his map of 1516, but by then the name was firmly rooted in public usage.

To his own treatise Waldseemüller appended a letter purportedly written by Vespucci describing four voyages to the New World between 1497 and 1503. According to the letter, the Kings of Spain and Portugal had each sponsored two of Vespucci's voyages in order to obtain information about the territories allotted to them by the 1493 papal line of demarcation. The same letter in slightly different form had first been published in 1504. If what the letter says is true, Vespucci preceded Columbus to South America by one year and therefore deserves the honor of being its discoverer. But some historians have challenged the genuineness of the letter. They believe it to have been forged in Florence, without Vespucci's knowldge, in an endeavor to make Vespucci, the Florentine, outshine Genoa's native son, Columbus. These historians argue that Vespucci actually made only the "2nd" and "3rd" voyages referred to in the letter. Whether the letter was forged or not, certainly it attracted enormous attention in the 16th century. Information about Waldseemüller and arguments on the Vespucci controversy are to be found in Frederick J. Pohl, *Amerigo Vespucci, Pilot Major* (New York, 1944) and in Germán Arciniegas, *Amerigo and the New World* (New York, 1955).

Cosmographiae Introductio

COSMOGRAPHIAE INTRODVCTIO CVM QVIBVS DAM GEOME TRIAE AC ASTRONO MIAE PRINCIPIIS AD EAM REM NECESSARIIS

Infuper quattuor Americi
Vefpucij nauigationes.

Vniuerfalis Cofmographiæ defcriptio tam
in folido ͵ plano / eis etiam infertis
quæ Ptholomęo ignota a nu
peris reperta funt.

DISTHYCON

Cum deus aftra regat / & terræ climata Cæfar
Nec tellus / nec eis fydera maius habent.

DIVO MAXIMILIANO CAESARI SEM
PER AVGVSTO GYMNASIVM
VOSAGENSE NON RVDIBVS
INDOCTISVE ARTIVM HV
MANITATIS COMMEN
TATORIBVS NVNC EX
VLTANS GLORIAM
CVM FOELICI
DESIDERAT
PRINCI
PATV.

SI MVLTAS ADIISSE REGIONES ET
populorum vltimos vidisse/ non solum voluptari‑
um: sed etiam in vita conducibile est'(quod in Pla‑
tone Apollonio Thyaneo atcp alijs multis philoso
phis qui indagandarum rerum causa remōtissimas
oras petiuerunt/clarum euadit.) Quis o Cæsar in‑
Bœtius nictissime regionum atcp vrbium situs/ & externo
rum hominum.
Quos videt condens radios sub vndas
Phœbus: extremo veniens ab ortu:
Quos premunt septem gelidi Triones:
Quos Nothus sicco violentus æstu
Torret ardentes recoquens harenas:

Quis inquã illornm omniu ritus ac mores/ex li
bris cognofcere: iucũdum ac vtile effe inficias ibit?
Sane(vt fapientũ fert opinio) ficut longiffime per
egrinari laudabile eft/ ita de quouis mortalium cui
perimenfus ipfæ terrarum orbis vel ex fola charta
rum traditione longę latecȝ fpectabilis atcȝ cogni
tus eft non abfurde repeti poteft quod ab ipfo poe
tarum principe Homero mufa Clyo de Naricio du   Home
ce verbis iftis rogabatur.   rus

Dic mihi mufa virum captæ poft tempora Troie

Qui mores hominum multorum vidit & vrbes

Hinc effectum eft/vt nobis(qui librariam offici
nam apud Lotharingie Vofagũ in oppido cui vo
cabulũ eft fancto Deodato/ nuper ereximus)Ptho
lomęi libros poft exemplar græcum recognofcẽti
bus:necnõ quattuor Americi Vefpucij nauigatio
nũ luftratiões adijcientibus:totius orbis typum tã
in folido cȝ plano(velut pręuiã quandã yfagogen)
pro communi ftudioforum vtilitate parauerimus.
Quẽ tuę facratiffimę maieftati/cũ terrarum dñs ex
iftas dicare ftatuimus. Rati nofipfos voti compo
tes & ab emulorum machinamentis tuo (tam cȝ
Achillis) clipeo tutiffimos fore / fi tuæ maieftatis
acutiffimo in eis rebus iudicio/ aliquantula faltem

A ij

ex parte nos satiffecisse ītellexerimus. Vale cæsar in inclytiffime. Ex superius memorato sancti Deodati oppido. Anno post natum Saluatorē supra sesqui＊ milleſimum septimo.

¡TRACTANDORVM ORDO

Cum Cosmographię noticia sine pręuia quadā astronomię cognitione/ & ipsa etiam astronomia sine Geometrię principijs plene haberi nequeat: di cemus primo in hac succincta introductiōe paucu＊ la de Geometriæ inchoamentis ad spheræ materia lis intelligentiam seruientibus.

2 Deinde quid sphera/axis/ poli &c.
3 De cœli circulis.
4 Quandam ipsius sphęræ secundum graduū ratio＊ nes Theoricam ponemus.
5 De quincȝ Zonis cœlestibus earumdemcȝ & gra＊ duum cœli ad terram applicatione.
6 De Paralellis.
7 De climatibus orbis.
8 De ventis cū eorȝ & aliarū rerū figura vniuersali
9 Nono capite quędā de diuiſiōe terrę/de finibus ma ris/de insulis/ & locorȝ ab inuicē distātia dicent̄.
Addetur etiam quadrans Cosmographo vtilis.
Vltimo loco q̄tuor Americi Vespucij subiūgent̄: p fectiōes. Et Cosmo. tā solidā q̄ȝplanā describemus.

DE PRINCIPIIS GEOMETRIAE AD SPHERAE NOTICIAM NECESSARIIS.
CAPVT PRIMVM

VIA IN SEQVENTIBVS circuli/circumferentię/centri/ diametri/ & id genus aliorum crebra mentio fiet: ideo primum nobis fingillatim/ de talibus breuiffimę tractandum venit.

Eft igitur Circulus/ figura plana vna quidem cir cumducta linea contenta: in cuius medio punctus eft/ a quo omnes rectæ lineę ad circūdantem lineā eductę ad inuicem funt æquales.

Figura plana/eft cuius medium nō fubfultat/neɜ ab extremis egreditur.

Circūferentia/ eft linea circulū continens ad quā omnes rectæ lineę a cētro circuli eiectę ínter fe funt æquales/quę & ambitus/ & circuitus/curuaturaɜ ac circulus a latinis/ græce autē peripheria diciū.

Centrum circuli/ eft punctus ille/ a quo omnes rectæ ad lineam circulum continentē eductę ad in uicem funt æquales.

Dimidius circulus/eft figura plana diametro cir culi & medietate circūferentię contenta.

Diameter circuli/eft quęcūɜ linea recta per cen

trum circuli transiens vtrincʒ ad circuli peripheri
am eiecta.

Linea recta / est a puncto ad punctum extensio
breuissima.

Angulus est duarum litterarʒ mutuus contactus
Est enim figuræ particula a lineę contactu in ampli
tudinem surgens.

Angulus rectus / est angulus ex linea supra lineã
cadente / & vtrincʒ altrinsecus duos ad inuicẽ ęqua
les angulos faciente causatus: quẽ si rectæ lineę con
tinẽt rectilineus: si curę / curuus spheraliscʒ dicetur
Obtusus est q̃ est recto maior. Acutus recto minor

Solidum / est corpus longitudine / latitudine / alti
tudinecʒ dimensum.

Altitudo / crassicies / profunditas idem.
Integrum est res tota / aut rei pars quæ sexagenaria
partitione non prouenit.

Minutum / est sexagesima integri pars.
Secundum / sexagesima pars minuti.
Tertium sexagesima secundi: & ita deinceps.

Caput secundum.   Quid sphera axis
poli &c̄. strictissime perdocet.

Antea q̃ aliquis Cosmographię noticiã haberi
possit / necessum est vt spheræ materialis cognitio
nem habeat. Postquod vniuersi orbis descriptioũe
primo a Ptholomęo atcʒ alijs traditam / & deinde
per alios amplificatã / nuper vero ab Americo Ve

sputio latius illustratã facilius intelliget. Igit̃ sphera
(vt eam Theodosius in libro de spheris definit) est **Theo-**
solida & corporea figura vna quidẽ conuexa supfi **dosius**
cie contenta/in cuius medio punctus est/a quo om
nes rect̨ ad circumferentiam educt̨ ad inuicẽ sunt
ꝗuales. Et cum(vt neotericis placet)decẽ sint sphe
r̨ cœlestis fit materialis sphera ad instar octaug(q̃
quod stellifera sit aplanes dicitur) ex circulis artifi-
cialiter ad inuicem iunctis per virgulam & axẽ medium centrum(qų terra est)tangentem c̃oposita.

 Axis spher̨/est linea per centrũ spher̨ transiens
ex vtraꝗ parte suas extremitates ad spher̨ circ̃ofe
rentiam applicans: circa quam sphera/sicut tota cir
ca axem carri(qui stipes teres est) intorquetur &
conuertitur/ estꝗ ipsius circuli diametrus. De quo
Manlius ita loquitur.
Aera per gelidum tenuis deducitur axis.
Sydereus medium circa quem voluit**u**r orbis:

Man-
lius.

 Poli (qui & cardines & vertices dicuntur) sunt
puncta cœli axem terminantia/ ita fixa vt nũꝗ mo
ueantur sed perpetuo eodem loco maneant. Et qų
hic de axe ac polis dicuntur ad octauã spheram re-
ferenda sunt. Quoniam in pr̨sentiarum materialis
sphere determinatiõe/q̃(vt diximus) octaug sphe
r̨ similitudinem habet/ suscepimus. Sunt itaꝗ eorum duo principales/ vnus septentrionalis (qui &
Arcticus & Borealis appellat̃ /alter Australis/ qũ

A iiij

¶Propositum est hoc libello quandam Cosmographiæ introductionē scribere: quam nos tam in solido q̃ plano depinximus. In solido quidem spacio exclusi strictissime. Sed latius in plano: vbi sicut agrestes signare asuecuerunt & partiri limite campum/ita orbis terrarum regiones præcipuas dominorum insigniis notare studuimus. Et (vt ab ea in qua sumus parte incipiamus) ad Europæ medrullium Rhomanas aquilas (quæ regibus Europæ dominantur) posuimus atq̃ daue summi patris patrū in signi ipsam fere Europam (quæ Rhomanam ecclesiam profitetur) cinximus. ¶Aphricam pene omnem & Asiæ partem signauimus lunulis quod est insigne summi Babilonis Soldā ni quasi totius Egypti & partis Asiæ domini. ¶Asiæ vero partē quæ minor Asia dicitur crocea coloris cruce iuncto chalybe circumdedimus quod est signū Thurcorū Soldani Scythiā intra imaū maximū Asie montē & Sarmaticā ¶Asiaticā notauimus anchoris quas magnns Tartarus pro insigni habet ¶Crux rubea presbyterum Ioannē (qui et orientali & meridionali Indiæ preest atq̃ in Biberith sedem tenet) repreſentat. Deniq̃ in quartam terræ partē per inclytos Castiliæ et Lusitaniæ reges repertam eorundem ipsorum insignia posuimus. Et quod nō est ignorandum vadosa maris littora (vbi naufragia timentur) imaginibus crucis signauimus sedihæc iam missa facientes.

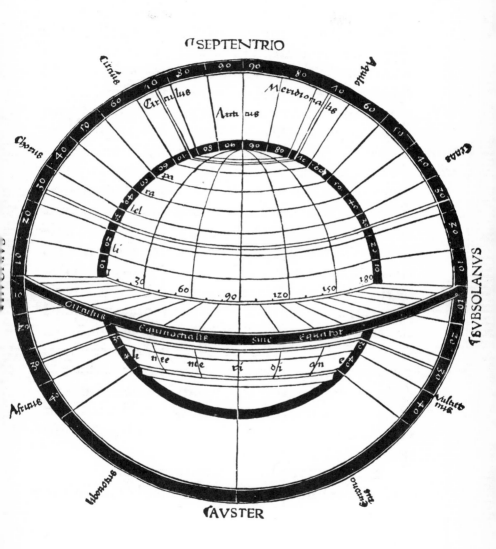

Virgil. Antarticum vocant/ de his Virgilius ait.
Hic vertex nobis semper sublimis/ at illum
Sub pedibus stix atra videt manesq; profundi.

Nos eñ iu Europa & Asia degētes polū Arctiẽ
cū ꝓpetuo videmus:q̃ sic diciꝰ ab Arcto vel Arctu
ro maiore Vrsa q̃ & Calisto & Elice nominatur &
septētrionales a septē stellis plaustri/ quæ Triones
vocitaꝸ:& sunt minoris Vrsæ/quam etiam Cyno
suram appellant. Vude Mantuanus Baptista.

Baptis. Tu nobis Elice nobis Cynosura/per altum.
Carme. Te duce vela damus &c̄. Itē Borealis & Aquiloʑ
nicus ab eius mundi parte vēto. Naute stellam maʑ
ris vocare assueuerunt. Huic oppositus est antarcti
cus:vñ & nomē sortiꝰ. Nam anti græca dictio latiʑ
ne cōtra significat. Is & Nothicus & Austronothi
cus diciꝰ:atcp a nobis ꝓpter terrę circulū qui est deʑ
uexus videri nō pōt:sed ab antipodibus(q̃s esse cō
pertū est)cerniꝰ. Vbi & orbiter annotādum/ quod
deuexū/rei sphericę tumorē & ventrem siguificat.
Conuexū ⱳo eius cōtrariū est/& cōcanitatē notat.
Sunt præterea duo alij poli ipsius zodiaci/ duos in
cœlo circulos arcticū.s. & antarcticū describentes.
Verū quia zodiaci & arctici atcp antarctici (qui in
cœlo sunt circuli)mentionē fœcimus: ideo capite se
quenti de circulis tractabimus.

De circulis cœli. Caput tertium.

Duplices sunt circuli q̃ & segmīa ab auctoribus

RVDIMENTA

dicuntur in sphera & cœlo/nõ reuera quidē existē✦
tes sed imaginabiles:maiores.s.& minores.

Maior circulus is est/qui incõuexa superficie sphe
ræ descriptus ipsam in duo æqua diuidit/horū sunt
sex.Aequator.s.Zodiacus/Colurus æquinoctiorꝛ/
Colurus solsticiorꝛ/ Meridianus/ & Horizon.

Circulus minor in sphera est/qui in eadē spheræ
superficie descriptus spheram minime in duo æqua
diuidit.Tales sunt quattuor.Arcticus/Cancri/Ca✦
pricorni/& Antarcticus.Ita summatim sunt decem
de quibus debita serie & primo quidem de maiori✦
bus dicemus.

Aequator(qui & primi mobilis cingulus & æqui
noctialis dicitur)est circulus maior spheram in duo
æqualia diuidens/secundum quamlibet sui partem
ab vtroꝗ polo æque distans: sic dictus quoniam so
le ipsum transeunte(quod bis in anno in principio
arietis.s.mense Martio/& principio libræ mense se✦
ptembri contingit) toto terrarum orbē æquinocti✦
um & dies nocti æqualis est.

Aequinoctiū Marcij/arietis/ vernale.

Aequinoctiū Septembris/libræ/ authumnale.

Zodiacus/est circulus maior æquatorem in duo
bus punctis quæ sunt principia arietis & libræ/ diri✦
mens/cuius vna medietatū ad Septentrionē/altera
vero ad Austrum declinat.Ita dictus vel a zodion
quod animal significat/qm̄ duodecim animalia in

ſe habet/vel a zoe quod eſt vita: quia oīm inferioꝶ
rum vita ſecundū planetaꝶ motus ſub ipſa eſſe di⸗
guoſcit.Latini eū ſigniferū vocāt: ꝗ. xij. ſigna in ſe

Virgiľ. ferat.Atꝗ obliquū circulū.Hinc & Maro infit.Ob
liquus qua ſe ſignorum verteret ordo.

In media zodiaci latitudine circularis linea ipſum
in duo æqua partiēs & vltro citroꝗ ſex latitu. graꞏ
relinquens intelligit:quā eclipticā vocant/eo quod
nunꝗ ſolis aut lunæ deliquiuū & eclipſis cōtingat
niſi eorum vterꝗ ſub ea linea in eodem vel oppo⸗
ſitis gradibus decurrat. In eodem ſi ſolare futurum
ſit deliquium.In oppoſitis vero ſi ipſius lunꝗ. Et ſol
ſemper ſub ea linea medius incedit/neꝗ vltro deui
at. Luna autem & cæteri planetarum nunc ſub ea
nunc citra vel vltra expaciati vagantur.

Duo ſunt in ſphera coluri/ qui ſolſticia & æqui⸗
noctia diſtinguunt.Ita a Colon græce quod mem⸗
brum ſignificat/& vris bobus (quos magnitudine

Cæſar Elephantum Cæſar cōmentarioꝶ lib.iiij. in Herci
nia ſilua eſſe ait)dicti/quoniā ſicut cauda bouis mē⸗
brum erecta ſemicirculum & non completum facit
ita nobis colurus ſemꝑ imperfectus apparet. Vna
enim medietas videtur/ cum alia ſit occultata.

Colurus ſolſticiorū qui & declinationū dicitur
eſt circulus maior per principia cancri & capricor⸗
ni/ꝑ polos eclipticꝗ parit & polos mundi tranſiens

Aequinoctioꝶ colurus itidem circulus maior eſt

per principia arietis ac librę/ & mūdi polos trāsiēs.

Meridianus eſt circulus maior per punctū verti⸗ **5**
cis & polos mundi tranſiens. Tales in generalibus
noſtris tam ſolido ꝗ̃ plano decē gradibus ab inui⸗
cem diſtinximus. Eſt autē punctū verticis(quod et
zenith dicit̄)in cœlo pūctus directe rei ſuppoſitus.

Horizon(quem finitorem quoꝗ dicūt)eſt ſphe⸗ **6**
ræ circulus maior ſuperius hemiſpherium(id eſt di
midiū ſpheræ)ab inferiori diuidens. Eſtꝗ is in quē
ſub diuo conſiſtentiū/circūducentiūꝗ oculos vide
tur obtutus deficere:qui & partem cœli viſam a nõ
viſa dirimere cernit̄. Diuerſarū autē regionum vari
us eſt horizon:& omnium horizontiū capitis ver⸗
tex/polus dicitur. Nam tale punctū omniquaꝗ ab
finitore atꝗ ipſo horizonte æque diſtat. Et hæc de
circulis maioribus/ nunc ad minores veniamus.

Circulus arcticus eſt circulus minor quem polus **7**
zodiaci ad motum primi mobilis circa polum mun
di arcticum deſcribit.

Antarcticus/ eſt circulus minor quē alter polus **8**
zodiaci circa polum mūdi antarcticum cauſat atꝗ
deſcribit. Nuncupamus autem polum zodiaci(de
quo etiam ſuperiori capite diximus) punctū vnde⸗
cunꝗ ab ecliptica ęque diſtantem. Sunt enim poli
zodiaci axis eclipticæ extremitates. Et ꝗ̃ta eſt ma⸗
xima ſolis declinatio (de qua mox plura) tanta eſt
poli zodiaci a polo mundi diſtantia.

Tropicus Cancri/eſt circulus minor quem ſol in principio cancri exiſtens ad motũ primi mobilis de ſcribit/qui & ſolſticium ęſtiuum dicitur.

Tropicus Capricorni/eſt circulus minor quẽ ſol initiũ capricorni tenens ad motũ primi mobilis deſ ſcribit.Hunc etiam circulum brumę dicimus.

Cæterum quia declinationis mentionẽ fœcimus ideo annotandum.

Declinationẽ eſſe quando ſol de ęquinoctiali ad Tropicum cancri ſcandit/vel ad capricorni tropicũ a nobis deſcendit.

Aſcenſionẽ pro contrario accipimus/qñ.ſ.a troꝰ picis æquatori propinquat. Licet a cyros & impro prie a quibuſdam dicaꝰ aſcendere quando nobis ꝓ pinquat/ & deſcendere cũ a nobis diſcedit. Hacteꝰ nus de circulis/iam ad ſpherę Theoricã & latiorem quandam graduum quibus tales ab inuicem diſtẽt ſpeculationem accedamus.

CAPVT QVINTVM
De quadam ſpherę Theorica ſe
cundum graduum rationes.

Sphera cœleſtis quincᷗ ligatur circulis principaꝰ lioribus vno maiore & quattuor minoribus.Arcti co.ſ.cancri/ęquatore/capricorni/& antarctico.E ꝗ bus ęquator eſt maior/alij quattuor minores. Hos ipſos vł potius ꝗ interſunt ſpacia authores Zonas Virgił. vocare aſueuerũt. Hinc & Virgilius in Georgi.ait.

Quinq̃ tenent cœlum zonæ: quarũ vna chorufco
Semper fole rubeus/ & torrida femper ab igni eſt
Quam circum extremę dextra læuacꝗ trahuntur
Cerulea glacie concretæ atcꝗ himbribus atris:
Has inter mediamcꝗ duæ mortalibus ægeris
Munere conceſſæ diuum:& via fecta per ambas
Obliquus qua fe fignorum verteret ordo.

De quarꝗ qnalitāte in fequentibus plura dicent̃.
Quia vero fupius tetigimus cꝗ polus Zodiaci cir∢
cnlum arcticum defcribat:ideo pro vlteriori fpecu∢
latione fciendum hoc de fuperiori Zodiaci polo
(qui in. 66. gradu &. 9. miñ.eleuationis fitus eſt at
cꝗ a polo arctico. 28. gradibus ac. 51. miñ.diſtat) iñ
telligi oportere.

Vbi & illud nõ ignorandum. Gradum tricefimã Grad:
figni partem eſſe. Et fignum duodecimam circuli. Signn:
At triginta duodecies multiplicata.360. reddunt.
Quare liquidum euadit qnod gradus iterũ tricente
fima & fexagefima circuli pars eſſe definiri poſſet.

Circulum antem antarcticum polus zodiaci infe
rior defcribit: qui in eodem gradu declinationis fi∢
tus eſt/ & æque a polo antarctico diſtat ficut fnpe∢
rior ab arctico.

Tropicũ cancri/ ecliptiç reflexio/ fiue **maxima**
folis verfus feptentrionem declinatio(quæ ab æqui
noctiali ad.33.grad.&. 51. miñ.fita eſt) defignat.

Tropicũ capricorni/alia eclypticæ reflexio/ fiue

B

maxima folis verfus Auftrum declinatio(quę ad to tidem gradus ficut prædicta fita eft) defcribit.

Diftantia inter tropicū cancri & circulum arcti cum eft. 22. graduum &. 18. miñ. Totidem etiā gra duum eft diftantia inter tropicum capricorni & cir culum antarcticum.

Aequatorem media cœli amplitudo a polis mun di æque diftans efficit.

Huc vſcʒ de quincʒ zonis & earum ab inuicem diftantia: conſequenter etiam ſtrictim de reliquis quędam trademus.

Circulum zodiaci eius ipſius poli oſtendunt/ a quibus vſcʒ ad tropicos(id eft maximas folis decli nationes & folfticia). 22. grad. &. 18. miñ. funt. Eft cʒ zodiaci latitudo ab ecliptica verſus vtroſcʒ tro picos fex graduum & in vniuerfum. 12. grad.

Coluros declinationū & afcenfionū fignant fol fticia & ęquinoctia/ hijcʒ fub polis mundi fefe per axem cœli ad angulos rectos fpherales interfecant. Similiter per ęquatorē. Sed p zodiacū ęquinoctio rum coluri vadentes conftituūt angulos obliquos cum per folfticiorum zodiaci rectos cauſent.

Circulnm meridionalem(mobilem quidem)axis idem fub ipſis polis continet.

Horizontis circulū/declarat zenith. Ipſum enim tancʒ polus eius fuperior exiftēs vbicʒ ab eo æque diftat. Atcʒ diuidit idem circulus horizontis/hemi

ſpheriū noſtrū ab altero per ſolis ortū & occaſum.
His vero qui ſnb æquinoctiali ſunt per vtroſcꝫ mū
di polos. Et diſtat ſemper zenith in omni horizon
te ab ipſius circūferentia. 90. gradibus qui ſunt quar
ta pars circuli. Eſtcꝫ peripheria horizontis quater
diſtantiam inter zenith & horizonta ſuperans.

Id demū animaduerſione nō eſt indignum axem
mundi in materiali ſphera diametraliter ab eiuſdem
polis per centrum muudi(quæ eſt terra)tranſire.

Axis vero zodiaci in ſphera nō apparet ſed intel
ligendus eſt:& hic axem mundi medium ad angu
los impares ſiue obliquos in centro interſecat.

Hoc modo in ipſa mundi fabrica mirabilis ſeries
& rerū ordo præcipuus eſſe videtur:cuius imaginē
veteres aſtronomi deſcribentes factoris ipſius quā
tum fieri potuit veſtigia(qui omnia in numero pon
dere & menſura ſœcit)ſequuti ſuut. Nos quocꝫ ea
de re tractantes ſpacij iniquitate ſic excluſi vt ratio
minutorum nō vel vix poſſit obſeruari/& ſi obſer
uaretur etiam tedium cum errore gigneret/ a plenis
graduum annotationibus circulorum poſitionem
ſumemus. Nam non multum diſtat inter. 51. miñ.
& plenum gradum qui ſexaginta minuta continet
ſicuti ſupradiximus:atcꝫ in libro de ſphera & aliubi
ab harum rerum ſtudioſis ex amuſſim declaratur.
Itacꝫ in figura / quam pro talium intelligentia hoc
loco ſubiungemus/ ipſi bini tropici cancri: ſcilicet

B ij

maxime folis declinatiõis ab equinoctiali. 2ℯ. gradibus diftabũt. Quãtũ & poli ipfius zodiaci/ fiue cir
culi arcticus & antarcticus a polis mũdi funt diftan
tes fuꝑ fexagefimũ fextũ eleuationis gradum fiti.

Polus Arcticus

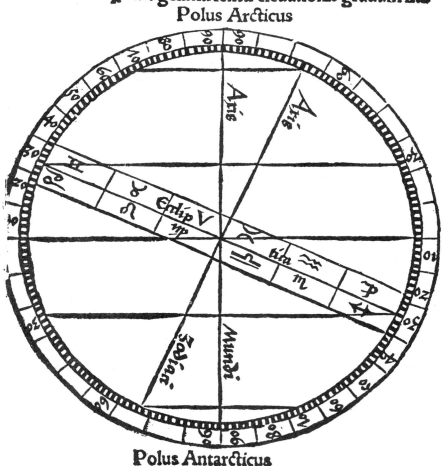

Polus Antarcticus

RVDIMENTA

De quinꝗ Zonis cœlestibus / earūdemꝗ
& graduū cœli ad terrā applicatione.
CAPVT QVINTVM

Hactenus breuiſſime de nŏuullis Geometriꝗ pri
cipijs / de ſphera / polis / quincꝗ zonis / atꝗ ipſis mū⸗
di circulis / rerūcꝗ taliū quadam Theorica diximus:
nūc recto (ni fallor) ordine de applicatione horū cir
culorū & graduū ad ipſam terrā ſuſcipienda deter⸗
minatio venit. Ergo igiſ ſciendū eſt in terra quincꝗ
plagas per zonas prꝗdictas diſtingui. vnde & Oui
dius in Methamorphoſi ait.

Vtcꝗ duæ dextera cœlum totidemcꝗ ſiniſtra
Parte ſecant zonꝗ / quinta eſt ardentior illis
Sic onus incluſum numero diſtinxit eodem
Cura dei: totidemcꝗ plagꝗ tellure premuntur
Quarū quæ media eſt non eſt habitabilis ꝗſtu
Nix tegit alta duas / totidem inter vtraſcꝗ locauit
Temperiemcꝗ dedit mixta cum frigore flamma.

Et vt res apertior fiat / quattuor minores circuli
Arcticus / cancri / capricorni / & antarcticus diſter⸗
minant diſtinguūtcꝗ quincꝗ cœli zonas. Vt (verbi
cauſa) eſto in ſequenti figura. a. polus mundi arcti⸗
cus. b. c. circulus boreus. d. e. circulus cancri. f. g. cir⸗
culus capricorni. h. k. antarcticus. l. ẙo polus nothi⸗
cus. Erit prima zona. ſ. Borea arcticacꝗ totū inter. b
a. c. interceptū ſpaciū / quꝗ perpetuo frigore rigens
inhabitata eſt. Secunda erit totum inter. b. c. & . d. e.

B iij

interceptũ fpaciũ/ temperata atcʒ habitabilis. Ter∕
tia totũ inter. d. e. f. g. mediũ fpacium feruore male
egrecʒ habitabilis. Sol eñ illic fcd'm lineã. f. e. (quæ
nobis ecliptica defignat)affidua volubilitate gyros
ducẽs fuo feruore eã reddit torridã atcʒ inhabitatã
Quarta eft totũ inter. f. g. &. h. k. fpaciũ temperata
atcʒ habitabilis/fi aquarũ vaftitas & altera cœli fa∕
cies id impune finat. Quinta eft totum inter. h. k. i.
interclufum fpacium frigore femper horrens atcʒ
inhabitata.

Cuṃ autē dicimus aliquã cœli zonã vel habitatã
vel inhabitatã/hãc denoiatione a fimili zona terræ
illi cœlefti plagę fubiecta itelligi volumus: & quan
do habitatam aut habitabilem dicimus/bene & fa
cile habitabilem. Cum vero inhabitatã vel inhabi∕
tabilē/egre difficilecʒ habitabilē intelligimus. Sunt
eñ qui exuftã torridamcʒ zonã nũc habitãt multi:
Vt q̃ Cherfonefum aureã incolũt/ vt Taprobanen
fes/Aethiopes:& maxima pars terrę femp incogni
tę nup ab Americo Vefpucio reptę. Qua de re ipfi
us quattuor fubiungentur nauigationes ex Italico
fermone in Gallicũ/& ex gallico in latiunm verfę.

Itacʒ fciendũ quod(vt & fubfequēs indicat figu
ra)prima zona q̃ polo arctico proxima eft. 23. gra∕
dus latitudinis &.51.miñ. habet.
Secunda quę antarctica atcʒ illi ipfi par eft/ totidē:
Tertia temperata.22.&.18.miñ.

RVDIMENTA

Quarta quæ pars est/totidem.
Quinta vo torrida & media gradus. 27. & 22: mi.
Sed horum quendam typum ponamus.

Polus Arcticus

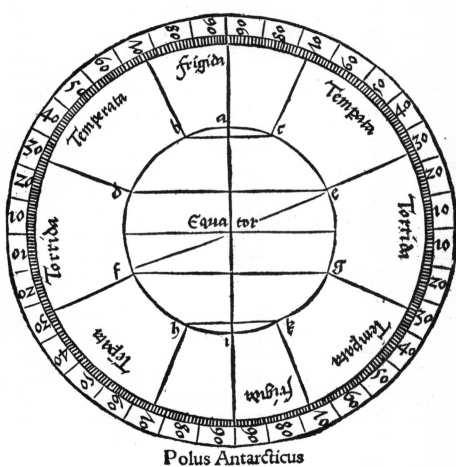

Polus Antarcticus

CAPVT SEXTVM
De paralellis.

Paralelli(qui ab Almucantharat dícunt̃)funt cir̄
culi vel lineę quoquo verſus / atꝗ ex omni parte
æquediſtantes/ & nunꝗ ſi poſſent etiam in infini̟
tum ꝑtrahi concurrētes. Qualis eſt in ſphera ęqua
tor cum alijs quattuor circulis minoribus. Nõ quia
quantũ primus a ſecundo/ tantum ſecundus a ter̟
tio diſtet:nam hoc falſum eſt: vt ex præcedentibus
liquet: ſed ꝗ quilibet duo circuli ſimul iunctí ſecun
dum quamlibet ſui partē æque ab inuicē ſint diſtan
tes. Non enim eſt æquator ex vna parte altero tro
picorum ꝗ ex alia vicinior aut diſtantior/ cum om
niquaꜯ a tropicis ſicut prædiximus . 23. gradibus
&.51. minutis diſtet.Simili modo de tropicis ad du
os extremos dicendum eſt: quorum vter ex omni̟
bus ſui partibus ab vtroꜯ. 2ꝛ. gradibus &.ꝛꝛ.mi̟
nutis diſtąnt.

Licet vero poſſent paralelli ad libitum cuinſlibet
diſtantes deſcribi nobis tamen pro faciliori ſuppu̟
tatione conuenietiſſimum viſum eſt(quod & ipſi
Ptholomęo placuit)vt tã in ſolida ꝗ plana Coſmo
graphiæ geueralis deſcriptione ipſos tot gradibus
ab inuicem ſecerneremns/ quot ſequens formula
oſtendit.Cui etiã figura ſubiungetur in qua paralel
los per terrã vtrimꜯ ad ſpheram cœli ꝑtrahemus.

Paralelli ab ęquat.	gradus cœli	Horę dierum ma.	Quot milli. fa. gra. vuus
21 Diatiles 8	63	20	28. ½
20	61	19	
19	58	18	23. ½
18	56	17	½
17	54	17	37. ½
16 Diarhip. 7	51. ½	16. ½	40. ½
15 Diabor. 6	48. ½	16	42. ½
14	45	15. ½	44
13	43. 1/12	15. ¼	45
12 Diarho. 5	40. ½. ⅓. 1/12	15	47
11	38. ½. 1/12	14. ½. ¼.	48. ½
10 Diarho. 4	36	14. ½	50
6	33. ⅓	14. ¼	
8 Diaalex. 3	30. ⅓	14	54
7	27. ½. ⅙	13. ½. ¼.	
6 Diasienes. 2	23. ½. ⅓	13. ½	
5	20. ¼	13. ¼	57
4 Diamero. 1	16. ⅓. 1/12	13	
3	12. ½	12. ½. ¼	
2	8. ⅓. 1/12	12. ½	
1	4. ¼	12. ¼	59
Aeq̄tor a polis ęq̄ distās		12. cōtinuę	60
1	4. ¼	12. ¼	59
2	8. ⅓. 1/12	12. ½.	
3	12. ½	12. ½. ¼	
4 Diameroes.	16. ⅓. 1/12	13	
5	20. ¼	13. ¼	

Climata cū gradibus paralellorꝫ simul horas
Insinuat numeris ista figura suis.

Para. & cli.	Gradus	Horę	Milliaria
6 Antidiaſienes	23.¼⅓	13.½	52
7	27.¹¹⁄₂₀	13,¹¹⁄₁₂	

Et ita deinceps verſus Antarcticū polū. Quod
& ſubſequens figura cōmonſtrat.

polus Arcticus

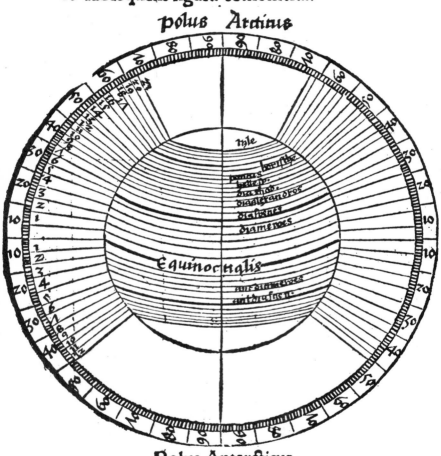

Polus Antarcticus

De climatibus caput. vij.

Licet clima propriæ regio interprętetur/hoc ta
men loco spacium terrę inter duas ęque distātes ap
pellatur/in quo porrectissime diei ab initio climatis
vsc̨z ad finem dimidiæ horæ variatio est. Et quottũ
aliquod clima ab ęquatore fuerit/tot semihoris lon
gissima eius loci dies superat diem nocti æqualem.
Suntc̨z ipsorum septem gemina: c̨znis ad austrum
nõ sit septimum adhuc lustratum. Sed Boream ver
sus Ptholomęus terram septem semihorarũ spacio
hospitalem & habitabilem inuenit: quę septē clima
ta ab insigni aut vrbe/aut flnuio/aut monte sua no
mina sunt sortita.

Primũ dicitur Dia Meroes/a dia quod apud grę
cos per significat/& casu patrio iungiẗ. Atc̨z a Me
roe q̃ est Affricę ciuitas in torrida zona citra ęqua
torem.16.gradibus sita/in quo paralello & ipse Ni
lus esse inuenitur. Eius/ & subsequētium etiã initiũ
medium & finem atc̨z maximę diei in quolibet ipo
rum horas generale nostrũ(pro cuius intelligentia
hæc scribimus) tibi liquido ostendet.

Dia Sienes a Siene Aegipti vrbe/quod est pro
uinciæ Thebaidos principium.

Dia Alexandrias. Ab Alexandria insigni vrbe
Affricæ Aegipti Metropoli:quam Alexander ma
gnus condidit:de quo dictũ est a poeta. Vnus pel
lco iuueni non sufficit orbis.

2 Dia Rhodon/ a Rhodo Afię minoris infula:quę
& fui nominis in ea fitam noftra tempeftate clarã

Rho- ciuitatem habet/ fortiter Thurcarum efferos belli-
dos cofcp impetus fuftinentem/ atcp profligantem ge-
nerofiffime.

5 Dia Rhomes:ab vrbe Europę notiffima/inter Ita
licas maxime clara/ & infigni olim gentiũ domitri-
ce/atcp orbis capite/ nũc patris patrũ maximi fede.

6 Dia Borifchenes/ a magno Scytharũ fluuio qui
eft quartus ab Hiftro.

7 Dia Rhipheon/a Ripheis mõtibus qui in Sarma
rica Europa infignes funt ppetua niue candentes.

Ab his infignibus locis per qnę ferme climatum
linęę mediæ tranfeunt feptem climata(quæ Ptholo
męus pofuit) fua fortiuntur nomina.

Octauũ Ptholomęus non pofuit/cum illud terrę
(quodcuncp eft) ipfi incognitum a nuperioribus lu
ftratũ fit:& dicitur Diatyles/quod ipfius principiũ
(qui eft paralellus ab æquatore. 21.) rectiffime per
Tylen fit ptenfus. Eft antê Tyle feptentrionalis in

Virgil. fula/de qua Maro nofter. Tibi feruiet vltima Tile.

Et hæc de climatibus ab ęquatore feptentrionem
verfus.Pari modo dicendũ eft de eis quę funt vltra
ęquinoctialê ad Auftrũ/quorę fex cõtraria nomina
habentia funt luftrata et dici poffunt antidia Mero
es/ antidia Alexandrias / antidia Rhodon/ antidia
Rhomes/antidia Borifchenes:a græca pticula anti

RVDIMENTA

que oppositũ vel contra denotat. Atcp in sexto cli=
mate Antarcticũ versus/ & pars extrema Affricæ
nuper reperta & Zamziber/laua minor/ & Seula
insulç/ & quarta orbis pars(quam quia Americus
inuenit Amerigen/ quasi Americi terrã/siue Ame=
cam nuncupare licet)sitæ sunt. De quibus Australi
bus climatibus hæc Pomponij Mellç Geographi
verba intelligenda sunt/ vbi ait. Zone habitabiles
paria agunt anni tempora/verum non pariter. An=
tichthones alteram/nos alteram incolimus. Illius si=
tus ob ardorẽ intercedẽtis plage incognitus/ huius
dicendus est. Vbi animaduertendum est quod cli=
matum quodcp alios cp aliud plerumcp foetus pro=
ducat/cum diuersç sunt naturæ/ & alia atcp alia sy=
derum virtute moderentur. Vnde Virgilius.
Nec vero terrç ferre omnes omnia possunt
Hic segetes/ illic veniunt foelicius vuç
Arborei foetus alibi/atcp iniussa virescunt
Gramia. Nõne vides croceos vt Thmolos odores
India mittit ebur: mittunt sua thura Sabçi
At Calybes nudi ferrum: virosacp pontus
Castorea. Eliados palmas Epiros equarum &c.

CAPVT OCTAVVM
De ventis.

Quoniã in superioribus ventorũ aliquando in=
cidenter memores fuimus(cũ.s. polũ Boreũ/polum
Nothicum/ atcp id genus alia diximus/ & ipsorum

Ame=
rige
Põpo:
Melç

Virgil.

C

cognitio nōnihil momenti/ īmo magnā vtilitatem
ad Cofmographiam habere dignofcitur. ideo hoc
fubfequenti capite quędā de ventis(qui & fpiritus
& flatus dicuntur) trademus. Eft igitur ventus(vt
a philofophis definitur)exhalatio calida & ficca la/
teraliter circa terram mota &c̄.

Quia vero fol fecundū binos tropicos/& ipfum
ęꝗtorē triplicē ortū atꝗ occafum/ ęftiuałē.f. ęqno/
ctiałē/ac hyemałē feruat/& meridiei fifiterꝗ ipfius
feptētrionis vtrincꝗ fint latera/ quarꝗ q̄libet ꝓpriū
ventū habēt:ideo fūmatim.xij.funt vēti/ tres orien
tis/ tres occidētis/ totidē meridiei/ & medie noctis
totidē:ex qbus q̄ttuor q in fequēti formula mediū
locū tenebūt principaliores funt/ alij minus princi.

		Trop.	Oriens	Occidens.
	Collat.	Trop.Canc.	Cecias	Chorus
	Medij.	Aequator.	Subfolanus	Fauoni q & Zephi.
Vento/rum for ma.	Collat.	Trop. Cap.	Eurus qui & Vultur.	Affricus q & Lybs
	Collat.		Meridies	Media nox
		Euronothus	Septētrio
	Medij	Aufter/q & Nothus	Aquilo qui & Boreas.
	Collat.	Lybo nothus	Trachias q & Circius.

RVDIMENTA

Poetę tn̄ minus principales(q̄ & collaterales di-
cunt̄)p̄ principalioribus ex licētia(vt suus sibi mos
est) vsurpare consueuerunt. Hinc & Ouidius ait.
Eurus ad auroram Nabathęac̄ȝ regna recessit
Persidac̄ȝ & radijs iuga subdita matutinis.
Vesper & occiduo quæ littora sole tepescunt
Proxima sunt Zephiro: Scythiā/septēc̄ȝ Triones
Horrifer inuasit Boreas/contraria tellus
Nubibus assiduis/pluuioc̄ȝ madescit ab austro.

　　Est autē subsolani aura saluberrima/ quæ a sole
purior & subtilior alijs efficitur.

　　Zephirus caloris & humoris temperiem habēs
montium pruinas resoluit. Vnde est illud Virgilij
Liquit̄ & putris Zephiro se glęba resoluit.

　　Austri flatus crebro tempestatū/procellarū/atc̄ȝ
himbrium pręsagus est. Quare & Nazo insit. Ma
didis Nothus euolat alis.

　　Aglo suo rigore ā̄q̄s ligat/atc̄ȝ cōstringit. Virgil.
Et glacies hyems aquilonibus asperat vndas.

　　His de ventis Gallinariū nostrū multæ doctrinę
virū sequētes quattuor edere versiculos memini.
Eurus & Eoo flat Subsolanus ab ortu.
Flatibus occasum Zephirusc̄ȝ fauonius implent.
Auster in extremis Lybię & Nothus ęstuat oris.
Sudificus Boreas Aquiloc̄ȝ minatur ab axe.

　　Et licet venti septentrionales sint natura frigidi/
nihilo tamen minus quando torridam zonam per

Ouidi.

Virgil.

Ouidi.

Virgil.
Gallina
rius.

C ij

transeunt/ mitigantur:sicut & de Austro torridam.
Zonam antea ᶜᵖ ad nos veniat transeute/comper⸗
tum est. Quod sequentibus v ersibus insinuatur.
Quoᶜᵖ loco prodit gelidus furit Auster/& arctis
Cogit aquas vinclis/at dum per torrida flatu
Sydera transierit/ nostras captandus in oras
Commeat:& Boreę seuissima tela retorquet
 At contra Boreas nobis grauis/orbe sub imo
Fit ratione pari moderatis leuior alis.
Cætera mox varios qua cursus flamina mittunt
Immutant proprię naturam sedis eundo.
 Hucusᶜᵖ de ventis dictū sufficiat/ponamus nunc
harᶻ omniū figurā vniuersalē: in qua sint poli/ axes
cirruli cū maiores/tum etiam minores/oriens/occi⸗
dens/ quincᶻ zonæ/gradus lōgitudinis/ latitudinis

tam ipsius terrę ᶜᵖ coeli/paralelli climata venti &c.

CAPVT NONVM. De quibusdam
Cosmographiæ rudimentis.

 Omnē terrę ambitū ad coeli spacium puncti obti
nere rationē astronomicis demonstrationibus con
stat. Ita vt si ad coelestis globi magnitudinem con⸗
feratur/nihil spacij prorsus habere iudicet̄.Et huius
quidem tam exiguę in mundo regionis quarta fere
portio est quę Ptholomęo cognita a nobis animā⸗
tibus incolitur. Atcᶻ in tres partes hactenus scissa
fuit. Europam: Affricam/& Asiam.

RVDIMENTA

Europa ab occidente mari Athlantico/ a septē.
Britannico/ab oriente Thanai/Meotide palude:&
pōto:a meridie mari mediterraneo clauditur/habet
cp̄ in se Hispaniam/ Galliam/ Germaniā/ Rhetiam
Italiam/Græciam/& Sarmatiam. Sic dicta a filia re
dis Agenoris eius nominis:quę dum virginibns Ti
rijs comitata in marino littore puellati studio lude⸗
ret & canistra floribus stiparet/ ab Ioue in thaurū
niueum verso rapta illius tergo insedisse/& p̄ ęquo
ra ponti in Crętam delata terræ contra iacenti no⸗
men dedisse creditur.

Affrica ab occidente mari Athlantico/ a meridie
oceano æthiopico/ a septentrione mari mediterra⸗
neo/& ab ortu Nili flumine terminatur.Ea in se cō
plectitur Mauritanias Tingitanam & Cęsariensem
Libiam interiorem/ Numidiam(quā & Mapaliam
dicunt) minorē Affricā(in qua est Chartago Rho⸗
mani imperij olim pertinax æmula) Cyreneicam/
Marmaricam/Lybiam(quo etiā nomine tota Affri
ca a Libe rege Maurithanię appellatur)æthiopiā in
teriorē/ ægiptum &c̄.Et dicitur Affrica quod frigo
ris rigiditate careat.

Asia (quæ cæteras magnitudine & opibus lon⸗
gissime vincit) ab Europa Thanai fluuio/ atꝗ ab
Affrica Ischmo(qui in australē plagā distentus Ara
bię & ægypti sinum perscindit)secerniū. Hæc prin⸗
cipalissimas regiones habet Bithiniam/ Gallatiam/

Capadociam/ Pamphiliam/ Lidiã/ Ciliciã/ Arme
nias maiorem & minorem. Colchiden/ Hircaniam
Hiberiam/ Albaniam:& præterea multas quas fin
gillatim enumerare longa mora effet. Ita dicta ab ei
us nominis regina.

    Nunc vero & hee partes funt latius luftratæ/ &
alia quarta pars per Americũ Vefputium(vt in fe
quentibus audietur)inuenta eft:quã non video cur

Ame | quis iúre vetet ab Americo inuentore fagacis inge
rico | nij viro Amerigen quafi Ameriti terram/ fiue Ame
ricam dicendam:cum & Europa & Afia a mulieri
bus fua fortita fint nomina.Eius fitũ & gentis mo
res ex bis binis Americi nauigationibus quę fequũ
tur liquide intelligi datur.

    Hunc in modum terra iam quadripartita cogno
fcitur: & funt tres primæ partes cõtinentes: quarta
eft infula: cum omni quãcp mari circũdata cõfpicia
tur. Et licet mare vnũ fit queadmodum & ipfa tel
lus:multis tamen finibus diftinctum/ & innumeris
repletum infulis varia fibi noia affumit:quæ in Cof

Prifcia. | mographię tabulis confpiciuntur. & Prifcianus in
tralatione Dionifrj talibus enumerat verfibus.
Circuit Oceani gurges tamen vndicp vaftus
Qui ĝuis vnus fit/plurima nomina fumit.
Finibus Hefperijs Athlanticus ille vocatur
At Boreę qua gens furit Armiafpa fub armis
Diciĩ ille piger necnon Satur. idẽ mortuus eft alijs:

Vnde tamen primo conſcendit lumine Titan   Mare
Eoumcɜ vocant atcɜ Indum nomine pontum   Eoum
Sed qua deuexus calidũ polus excipit auſtrum   Indicũ
Aethiopumcɜ ſimul pelagus Rubrũcɜ vocatur   æthio
Circuit oceanus ſic totum maximus orbem   picum;
Nominibus varijs celebratus.

Perſecat Heſperiam primus qui porgitur vndis
Pamphilcũcɜ latus Lybiȩ prȩtendit ab oris   Pãphi
Sic minor eſt reliquis/maior quẽ Caſpia tellus   licum.
Suſcipit intrantem vaſtis aquilonis ab vndis
Nomine Saturni quod Thetis poſſidet ȩquor   Caſpiũ
Caſpius iſte ſinus ſimul Hircanuſcɜ vocatur

    At duo qui veniunt auſtralis ab ȩquore ponti   Hirca
Hic ſupra currens mare Perſicus efficit altum   Perſiũ
E regione ſitus/ qua Caſpia voluitur vnda.

    Fluctuat aſt alter Panchȩacɜ littora pulſat
Euxeni contra pelagus protentus in auſtros.

    Ordine principiũ capiens athlantis ab vnda   Athlan
Herculeo celebrant quam mȩte munere Gades: ticum.
Cȩliferaſcɜ tenet ſtans athlas monte columnas   Hercu
Eſt primus vaſtis qui pontus Hibericus vndis   leum.
Diuidit Europen Lybia communis vtricɜ
Hinc atcɜ hinc ſtatuȩ ſunt: ambȩ littora cernunt
Hȩc Lybies hȩc Europes aduerſa tuendo.
Gallicus hunc gurges:qui Celtica littora pulſat   Gallicũ
Excipit: hunc ſequitur Ligurũ cognomine dictus
Qua domini rerum terris creuere latinis.
    Ad petram leucen aquilonis ab axe reductus

COSMOGRAPHIAE

Quæ freta Sicanię concludit littere curuo
Infula fed Cyrnos proprijs pulfatur ab vndis.

Mare
Thyrre
    Intra fardonium pelagus Celtumcʒ refufis
Inde falis tumidus Tyrrheni voluitur ęftus
Ad partes vergens auftrales/ excipit iftum

Siculū
Sicanię gurges folis deflexus ad ortus:
Qui procul effufus Pachynis tenditur oris
Ad Creten fummā(quæ prominet ęquore) rupem
Qua Gortyna potens medijs qua Phęftos in aruis
Arietis hanc rupem fimilantem vertice frontem
Pro merito graij Criu dixere metopon.
Hoc mare Gargani concludit lapygis oras

Adriati
cum
Ioniū
    Illinc incipiens extenditur Adria vaftus:
Ad Boream penetrans pellago folemcʒ cadentē.
    Ionius pariter finus hic perhibetur ab orbe:
Diuidit & geminas diuerfis partibus oras:
Quas tamen extremas cōiungit terminus vnus

Illiricū
    A dexteram partē proteriditur Illyris alma:
Poft hanc Dalmatię populorꝛ martia tellus
Ad lęuam Aufonię porrectus continet Ifthmos
Quē tria circūdant maria vndicʒ littore curuo
Tyrrhenum/Siculam/necnō fimul Adria vaftus
Finibus at proprijs exceptant fingula ventos
Tyrrhenum Zephyro: Siculum fed tūdiť auftro.
Adria fuccurrens Eoo frangitur Euro.
    At poft Sicaniam tractu diffunditur alto

Syrtis
Ad Syrtim pelagus/ Lybicis quę cingitur oris:

Maiorem poftĝ minor excipit:ęquora longe
Atĝ finu gemino refonantia littora pulfant
  Finibus a Siculis Cretęum tenditur ęquor   **Mare**
Ad folis veniens ortus Salmonida pofcens   **Creteũ**
Dicitur Eous qui Cretę terminus effe.
  Poft hanc geminũ mare vaftũ fluctibus atris:
Fluctibus Hifmarici Bor_ę_ quod tundit atris.
Quod ruit aduerfus celfę de partibus arcti
Quod prius eft phariũ phibēt:hoc littora tāgit   **Phariũ**
Pręcipitis cafu montis:poft vnda fecunda
Sidoniũ eft pelagus: penetrat qua gurgite pontus   **Sidoni-**
Ificus arctoas ad partes æquore vergens   **um**
Non longe rectus. Cilicum nam frangitur oris:
Hinc Zephiros pofcens veluti draco flectit vndis
Quod iuga montiuagus vaftat:filuafĝ fatigat:
Partibus extremis Pamphilia clauditur ifto:
Atĝ Chelidonię rupes cinguntur eodem
At procul hunc zephyrus finit Patareide fumma
  Poft hæc arctoas ad partes afpice rurfus   **Aegeũ**
Aegeum/fuperat qui fluctibus ęquora cuncta:
Difperfas vafto qui gurgite Cycladas ambit
Terminat hunc imbros pariter Tenedofĝ coercēs
Angufta trahitur/qua fauce Propontidis vnda
Afia:quam fupra populis difttenditur amplis
Ad Notiam partem:qua latus ducitur Ifthmos:
Threicius fequitur poft Bofphorus oftia ponti: **bofpho-**
Hoc nullum perhibent terras anguftius orbis   **rus.**
                        D

COSMOGRAPHIAE

Symple
gades Esse fretum dirimens: hic snnt Symplegades arct,
Panditur hic ponti pelagus Titanis ad ortus
Quod petit obliquo Boream solemeq meatu
Hinc atcq hinc medio percurrunt equore colles:
Vnus qui veniens Asię de parte Carambis
Dicitur australi: sed contra finibus alter
Prominet Europę hunc criu dixere metopon,
Ergo conueniunt aduersi gurgite tanto
Distantes quantū ternis transire diebus
Eualeat nauis:binarum sic equore pontum
Aspicias similem cornu quod flectitur arcus
Neruo curuati distento dextera neruum
Assimilat:recto trahitur nam linea ductu
Extra quā Boream quo scandit sola Carambis
Sed formam cornu geminatis flexibus edit
Littus:quod pontum cingit sub parte sinistra

Meotis In quam Meotis penetrans aquilionis ad axes
Quam Scythię gentes circundant vndicq ripis
Et matrem ponti perhibent Meotidis vndam,
Scilicet hic ponti vis exit gurgite multo

Thaurꝝ Cimmeriū torrens per Bosphoron hic vbi thaurū
Cimmerij gelidis habitant sub finibus imum
Hęc maris est species splendens hęc forma ꝓfundi,
Est autē vt ꝓdiximus marę plenū insulis e ꝗbus
maximę & pricipaliores iuxta Ptholomęū hę sunt,
Taprobana in mari Indico sub ęquatore
Albion quæ & Britannia & Anglia

Sardinia in mari mediterraneo
Candia quæ & Creta in sinu Aegeo?
Selandia
Sicilia   in mari mediterraneo
Corsyca
Ciprus

Extra Ptholomęum
Madagascar in mari Prasodo
Zamzibar
Iaua in Oceano Indico orientali
Angama
Peuta   In oceano Indico
Seula
Zipangri in Oceano occidentali
Hę sunt ingentes quas cingit Tethyos vnda
Insulę:adhuc alię diuersis partibus orbis.
Diuersę plures fama latuere minores
Auris difficiles nautis vel portubus aptę
Quarū nō facile est mihi promere noīa versu?

Priscia

Cæterū vt vnius loci ab altero distantiā cogno
scere possis poli eleuatio tibi cū primis cōsideranda
venit. Annotandū igiť paucis quod(vt ex superiori
bus liquet)viuētibus sub paralello ęqnoctiali vter
cʒ polus in horizonte est. Eunti autē ad septentrio
nem eo magis subleuať polus quāto plus aliquis ab
ęquatore discesserit. Quæ poli eleuatio regionum
& locorum ab æquatore distantiam demonstrat;

D ij

COSMOGRAPHIAE

Eſt em̄ tātus loci tractus ab ęquatore cuius mēſurā
ſcire deſideras/q̄nta eſt eleuatio poli ad zenith eiuſ
dē. Ex quibus milliariū numerus facilis cognitu eua
dit/dū eundē p̄ numerū eleuationis poli multiplica
ueris. Verū tn̄ non ſunt ſcd'm Ptholomęi ſententiā
milliaria a circulo ęqnoctiali ad arcton vbiꝗ gētiū
ęqualia. Nā primo ęquatoris gradu vſꝗ ad duode
cimū/q̄libet graduū ſexaginta Italicę milliaria con‑
tinet q̄ faciūt. 15. Germanica. Cōmuniter em̄ q̄ttuor
Italica pro vno Germanico reputant̄. Et a. 12. gradu
vſꝗ ad. 25. quilibet. 59. milliaria facit/quæ ſunt Ger
manis. 12. ½. ¼. Atꝗ vt res fiat apertior/ponemus
formulam ſequentem.

	Gradus	Gradus	Millia. Ital.	Mil. Ger.
Aequa‑tor.	1	12	60	15
Tropi‑cus.	12	25	59	14 ½ ¼
	25	30	54	13 ½
	30	31	50	12 ½
	31	41	41	11 ¼
	41 uſꝗ ad	51 faciūt	40	10
	51	51	32	8
	51	63	28	1
	63	66	26	6 ½
Circu. Arcti.	66	10	21	5 ¼
Polus Arcti.	10	80	6	1 ½
	80	90		0

Et ita quoc̄ɉ ab ęquinoctiali versus polos tā antarcticum c̄ɉ arcticum graduū latitudinis cōtinen-
tia variatur. Quod si scire volueris / quot ab vno
loco ad alium milliaria sint / perpende diligenter in
quibus gradibus latitudinis sint talia loca / & quot
gradus medient / deinde vide in formula superiori
quot milliaria talis gradus habeat / & multiplica nu
merū milliariū per numerū mediorᵹ graduum / atc̄ɉ
milliarium numerus resultabit: qnæ cum Italica sue
rint diuidas per quattuor / & Germanica habebis.
Hęc ͵p inductione ad Cosmographiā dicta sufficiāt   **Notes:**
si te modo ammouerimus prius / nos in depingēdis
tabulis typi generalis nō omnimodo sequutos esse
Ptholomęū / pręsertim circa nouas terras vbi in car
tis marinis aliter animaduertimus ęquatorē consti-
tui c̄ɉ Ptholomęus fœcerit. Et ͵pinde nō debēt nos
statim culpare qui illud ipsum notauerint. Cōsulto
em̄ fœcimus quod hic Ptholomęū / alibi cartas ma-   **Phtolo**
rinas sequuti sumus. Cū & ipse Ptholomęus quin-   **męus.**
to capite primi libri. Non omnes continentis partes ob suę magnitudinis excessum ad ipsius perue-
nisse noticiam dicat / & qualis quemadmodum se
habeant ob peregrinantium negligentiam sibi minus diligenter traditas / alias esse quas aliter atc̄ɉ ali
ter se habere cōtingat ob corruptiones & mutatio
nes in quibus pro parte corruisse cognitę sunt. Fuit
igitur necesse(quod ipse sibi etiā faciūdū ait)ad no-

APPENDIX

nas temporis noſtri/traditiões magis intendere. Et
ita quidē temporauimus rem: vt in plano circa no⸗
uas terras & alia quępiam Ptholomęum: in ſolido
vero quod plano addit deſcriptionē Americi ſubſe
quentem ſectati fuerimus.

APPENDIX

Annectamus adhuc ſuperioribus antea ꝗ̈ rece⸗
ptui canamus eleuationis poli atꝗ ipſius zenith ac
cētri horizontis & climatū quadrantē velut parer⸗
gon & quoddam corolariū. Quamuis ſi recte con⸗
ſiderauerimus is quadrans de quo dicemus non ſit
ad has res impertinēs. Coſmographū em̄ vel maxi
me poli ſupra caput eleuationē/zenith/& terrę cli⸗
mata cognoſcere oportet. Format itaꝗ idem qua⸗
drans hoc pacto. Diuide quēcunꝗ circulum in par
tes quattuor/ita quod duę diametri ſe in centro ad
angulos rectos inter ſecent: quarū vna (quæ altera
ſui parte pinnulas habet) axem polor̃ mundi/ & al
tera ęquatorem ſignificabit. Deinde eā parte circuli
quę eſt inter ſemiaxem pinnulas habentem/ & alte
ram ſemidiametrum in partes. xc. diuidas/ atꝗ op⸗
poſitā in totidem/figaſꝗ perpendiculū ad centrum
& paratus erit quadrans. Cuius hic eſt vſus. Verte
eū ita vt p pinnularū foramina polū directe videas
& ad qd’ clima atꝗ in quē gradū ꝑpendiculū ceci⸗
derit/eo ipſo climate & eleuatiōis gradu tua regio/
quinetiā zenith atꝗ horizontis centrū exiſtit.

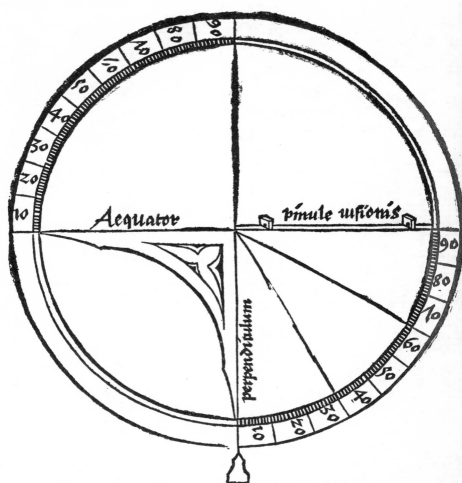

Hactenus exequuti capita ꝓpofita/ hic ipfas lon
ginꝙs expaciatiões fequēter ītroducamus Vefputiŋ
fingulorꝫ factorꝫ exitū circa inftitutū tradentes: ꝉ

Finis introductionis

QVATTVOR AMERICI VESPVTII NAVIGATIONES

Eius qui subsequentẽ terrarum
descriptionẽ vulgari Gal‑
lico in latinum
transtulit.

Decastichon ad lectorem:

Aspicies tenuem quisquis fortasse logiam
   Nauigium memorat pagina nostra placens:
Continet inuentas horas/gentesᵱ recenter
   Lętificare sua quę nouitate queant.
Hæc erat altiloquo prouincia danda Maroni
   Qui daret excelsę verba polita rei.
Ille quot ambiuit freta cantat Troius heros:
   Sic tua Vesputi vela canenda forent.
Has igitur lectu terras visurus/in illis
   Materiam libra:non facientis opus.

Item distychon ad eundẽ

Cum noua delectent fama testante loquaci
   Quæ recreare queunt hic noua lector habes:

α Τέλοϛ.

A

Philesius Vogesigena
Lectori

Nilus.	Rura papirifero qua florent pinguia Syro
Lacus	Et faciunt Lunę magna fluente lacus
Lunę.	A dextris mõtes sunt Ius/Danchis/ quocȝ Mascha
Ius.	Illorum æthiopes inferiora tenent
Dāchis	Aphrica cõsurgit quibus e regionibus aura
mascha	Afflans cum Libico seruida regna Notho:
æthio.	Ex alia populo Vulturnus parte calenti.
Aphri.	Indica veloci per freta calle venit.
Libono	Subiacet hic ęquo noctis Taprobana circo:
thus	Bassacȝ Prasodo cernitur ipsa salo
Vultur.	Aethiopes extra terra est Bassamcȝ marinā
Tapro-	Non nota e tabulis o Ptholomęe tuis.
bana.	Cornigeri zenith tropici cui cernitur hirci
Mare	Atcȝ comes multę funditor ipsus aquę.
Praso.	Dextrorsum īmenso tellus iacet ęquore cincta
	Tellus/quam recolit nuda caterua virum
Pars a-	Hanc quem clara suū iactat Lusitania regem
phricę ī	Inuenit missa per vada classe maris.
uenta.	Sed quid plura: situ/gentis morescȝ repertę
Ameri-	Americi parua mole libellus habet.
ge.	Candide syncero voluas hunc pectore lector
	Et lege nõ nasum Rhinocerontis habens.

ο ΤέΛοδ.

Illuſtriſſimo renato Iheruſalem & Siciliȩ
regi/duci Lothoringiȩ ac Barñ. Ame
ricus Veſpucius humilem re＊
uerentiam/ & debitam re＊
cõmendationem.

Fieri poteſt illuſtriſſime rex/vt tua maieſtas mea
iſta temeritate ducatur in admirationem:propterea
quod haſce litteras tam prolixas ad te ſcribere non
ſubuerear/cum tamen ſciam te continuo in arduis
conſilijs & crebris reipublicȩ negocijs occupatiſſi＊
mum. Atcɜ exiſtimabor forte nõ mõ p̄ſumptuoſus
ſed etiam ocioſus: id mihi muneris vendicans/vt
res ſtatui tuo minus conuenientes non delectabili:
ſed barbaro prorſus ſtilo(veluti amuſus ab huma＊
nitatis cultu alienus)ad Fernandum Caſtiliȩ regem
nominatim ſcriptas/ad te quocɜ mittã. Sed ea quã
in tuas virtutes habeo cõfidentia/ & comperta ſe＊
quentiũ rerũ/necɜ ab antiquis/necɜ neotericis ſcri＊
ptarum veritas me corã t. M. fortaſſis excuſabunt.
Mouit me imprimis ad ſcribendum prȩſentiũ lator
Beneuenutus. M. t. humilis famulus/& amicus me
us nõ pœnitendus/qui dum me Liſbone reperiret
precatus eſt:vt.t.M.rerũ p me quattuor profectio＊
nibus in diuerſis plagis mundi viſarum/participem
facere vellem. Peregi em̄ bis binas nauigationes ad
nouas terras inueniendas: quarũ duas ex mandato
Fernandi inclyti regis Caſtiliȩ p̄ magnũ oceani ſiꝏ̄

A ij

occidentẽ verſus fœci/alteras duas iuſſu Manuelis
Luſitaniẽ regis'ad Auſtrũ.Itacɜ me ad id negocij ac
cinxi ſperãs cɜ.t.M. me de clientuloɿ numero non
excludet:vbi recordabitur cɜ olim mutuã habueri⁄
mus inter nos amicitiã tᵱe iuuẽtutis nr̃ẽ/cũ grãma⁄
ticẽ rudimẽta imbibentes ſub ᵱbata vita & doctri
na venerabilis & religioſi fratris de.S. Marco Fra.
Georgij Anthonij Veſputij auunculi mei pariſ mi
litaremus.Cuius auunculi veſtigia vtinã ſequi po⁄
tuiſſem/alius ᵱfecto(vt & iᵱe Petrarcha ait)eſſem
cɜ ſum.Vtcũcɜ tñ ſit/nõ me pudet eſſe q̃ ſum. Sem
per em̃ in ipſa ẙtute & rebus ſtudioſis ſummã ha⁄
bui delectationẽ.Quod ſi tibi hẽ narrationes omni
no nõ placuerint.dicã ſicut Plinius ad Mẽcenatem
ſcribit.Olim facetijs meis delectari ſolebas. Et licet
M.t.ſine ſine in reipublicẽ negocijs occupata ſit:ni⁄
hilominus tm̃ tᵱis qñcɜ ſuffuraberis: vt has res cɜ⁄
uis ridiculas(quẽ tñ ſua nouitate iuuabũt)perlegere
poſſis. Habebis em̃ hiſce meis lr̃is poſt curarum ſo
mẽta & meditamẽta negocioɿ nõ modicã delecta
tionẽ/ſicut & ipſe fœniculus prius ſumptis eſculen
tis odorẽ dare & meliorẽ digeſtionẽ facere aſueuit;
Em̃ ẙo ſi plus ẽq̃ ᵱlixus fuero/veniã peto. Vale.
  Inclytiſſime rex ſciat.t. M. quod ad has ipſas re⁄
giones mercandi cauſa primũ venerim.Dumcɜ per
q̃drennij reuolutionẽ i eis rebus negocioſus eſſem
& varias fortunẽ mutatiões animaduerterem/atcɜ

videre quo pacto caduca & tranſitoria bona homi
nem ad tempus in rotę ſummo tenerent/ & deinde
ipſum præcipitarent ad imū qui ſe poſſidere multa
dicere poterat:conſtitui mecū varijs taliū rerū caſi
bus exanclatis iſtiuſmodi negocia dimittere/ & me
orum laborum finē in res laudabiliores ac plus ſta
biles ponere.Ita diſpoſui me ad varias mundi par
tes contemplandas/& diuerſas res mirabiles viden
das.Ad quam rem ſe & tempus & locus oportune
obtulit.Ipſę enim Caſtilię rex Fernādus tunc quat
tuor parabat naues ad terras nouas occidentē ver
ſus diſcooperiendas/cuius celſitudo me ad talia in
ueſtiganda in ipſam ſocietatem elegit. Et ſoluimus
vigeſima die Maij.M.cccc..xcvij. de portu Calicię
iter noſtrum per magnum oceani ſinū capientes:in
qua profectione.xviij.conſumauimus menſes/mul
tas inuenientes terras firmas/ & inſulas pene innu
merabiles vt plurimum habitatas/quarū maiores
noſtri mentionē nullā fœcerūt.Vnde & ipſos anti
quos taliū nō habuiſſe noticiā credimus. Et niſi me
moria me ſallat memini me in aliquo legere/qd'mą
re vacuum & ſine hominibus eſſe tenuerint. Cuius
opinionis ipſe Dantes poeta noſter fuit/vbi duo
deuigeſimo capite de inferis loquens Vliſſis mortē
confingit. Quę autem mirabilia viderim/in ſeqnen
tium proceſſu.t.M. intelliget.

A iij

PRINCIPIVM

TERRARVM infularumcp variarũ defcriptio quarum veftuti nõ meminerunt autores/ nuper ab anno ĩcarnati domini.M.cccc.xcvij. bis geminis na uigationibus in mari difcurfis/inuentarum:duabus videlicet in mari occidentali per dominũ Fernandũ Caftilię/ reliquis vero duabus in Auftrali ponto ꝑ dominũ Manuelem portugallię fereniffimos reges Americo Vefputio vno ex naucleris nauigiũcp pre fectis precipuo fubfequẽtem ad prefatũ dominum Fernandum Caftilię regem/ de huiufmodi terris & ĩnfulis edente narrationem.

ANNO DOMINI. M. CCCC. xcvij.xx. menfis Maij die/ nos cũ iiij. conferuãtię nauibus Calicium exeuntes portum/ad infulas(olim fortunatas/ nunc vero magnã Ca nariam dictas) in fine occidentis habitati pofitas in tertio climate: fuper quo extra horizontem earum fe.xxvij.gradibus cũ duobus tertijs/ feptentriona‑ lis eleuat polus/diftantefcp ab hac ciuitate Lifbona in qua confcriptum extitit hoccine præfens opufcu lum.cc.lxxx.leucis:vento inter meridiem & Lebec cium ventũ fpirante/curfu primo pertigimus. Vbi (nobis de lignis/aqua/ ceterifcp neceffarijs prouidẽ do) cofumptis octo fere diebus nos(facta in primis ad deum oratione) eleuatis dehinc & vẽto traditis

velis nauigationem noſtrã per ponentẽ incipientẽ
(ſumpta vna Lebeccij quarta) tali nauigio trãſcur
rimus.vt.xxvij. vix elapſis diebus terrę cuidam ap
plicaremus/ quã firmã fore exiſtimauimus. Diſtat
ꝗ Canarię magnę ab inſulis. M. (vel circiter)leucis:
extra id quos in zono torrida habitatũ eſt. Q uod
ex eo nobis cõſtitit: ꝗ ſeptentrionalem polum ex
tra huiuſcemodi telluris horizontem. xvi. gradibus
ſe eleuare/ magiſꝙ occidentalem. lxxv. ꝗ magnæ
Canarię inſulas gradibus exiſtere conſpeximus: ꝓ
ut inſtrumenta omnia monſtrabãt. Q uo in loco(ia
ctis de prora anchoris)claſſem noſtrã/leuca a litto
re cũ media diſtantẽ/reſtare coegimus:nõnullis ſo
lutis phaſelis armis & gẽte ſtipatis/ cũ quibus ipm
vſꝗ ad littus attigimus. Q uo ꝗprimũ puenimus:
gentẽ nudã ſcdm littus euntẽ innumeram percępi
mus. Vnde non paruo affecti fuimus gaudio. Om
nes eñ qui nudi incedere conſpicebant: videbant
quoꝗ ꝓpter nos ſtupefacti vehęmẽter eſſe. Ex eo
(vt arbitror)ꝗ veſtitos/alteriuſꝗ effigiei ꝗ forent
nos eſſe intuiti ſunt. Hij poſtꝗ nos adueniſſe co
gnouerunt/omnes in propinquũ montẽ quendam
aufugerunt:a quo tũc nec nutibus/ nec ſignis pacis
& amicicię vllis/v t ad nos accederẽt allici potuerũt
Irruentc ẏo interea nocte/nos claſſem noſtrã male
tuto in loco(vbi nulla marinas aduerſus ꝓcellas
tuta reſidentia foret)cõſidere timentes: cõuenimus

A iiij

vna/vt'hinc(mane facto) difcederemus:exquirere∕
mufc₂ portū quēpiā/vbi nŕas ftatione in tuta collo
caremus naues. Qua de liberatiõe arrepta/nos vē∕
to fcďm collē fpiranti traditis velis/ poftc̄₂(vifu ter
ram ipfam fequēdo/atc₂ ipfo plagę in littore/gētes
continue percipiendo)duos integros nauigauimus
dies:locum nauibus fatis aptū comperimus. In quo
media tantū leuca diftantes ab arida/cõftitimus/ vi
dimufc₂ tunc inibi innumerabilē gentiū turbā/ qnã
nos cominus infpicere/ & alloq defiderantes:ipfa∕
met die littori cū cymbis & nauiculis noftris appro
piauimus: necnõ & tunc in terrā exiuimus/ ordine
pulchro.xl.circirer viri huiufcemodi gente fe tamē
a nobis & confortio noftro penitus alienā pręben∕
te.Ita vt nullis eā]modis ad colloquiū cõmunicatio
nemue noftrā allicere valuerimus: p̄ter illis paucos
quos multos poft labores ob fufceptos/tandem at
traximus ad nos dando eius nolas/ fpecula/ certos
criftallinos aliac₂ fimilia leuia/qui tum fecuri de no
bis effecti/conciliatum nobifcū/necnon de pace &
amicicia tractum venerūt. Subeūte autem interim
nocte/nos ab illis nofmet expedientes(relictis eis)
noftras ingreffi fumus ad naues. Poftea vero fub∕
fequentis fummo diluculo diei/ infinitam in littore
virorum & mulierum paruulos fuos fecum vectan
tium gentem'rurfum confpeximus cognouimufc₂
multitudinē illa fuppellectilem fuā fecū deferre totā

qualē infra ſuoʾlocū dicet̃. Quorꝛ complures c̃ꝓpri
mū terrę appropiauimus ſemet in ęquor eproijciē⸗
tes(cum maximi natatores exiſtant)quantus eſt ba
liſtę iactus nobis venerunt natantes obuiam/ſuſce
perūt nos humaniter: atcꝫ ea ſecuritate & confidē⸗
tia ſeipſos inter nos cōmiſcuerūt ac ſi nobiſcum diu
tius antea cōſueuiſſent & pariter frequētius practi
cauiſſent:pro qua re tūc haud parum oblectati fui⸗
mus. De quorum moribus(quales eos habere vidi
mus)hic/quādoquidem ſe cōmoditas offert/inter⸗
dum etiam interſerimus.

De moribus ac eorum
viuendi modis.

¶ Vantum aduerſum eorūcꝫ mores/omnes
tam mares fœminę nudi penitus incedunt
tectis/nō aliter verendis c̃ꝫ cū ex vtero ꝓ
dierunt.Hij mediocris exiſtentes ſtature multū be⸗
ne ꝓportionati ſunt quorꝛ caro ad ruſedinē(veluti
leonū pili)vergit:qui ſi veſtimentis operti mearent
albi(credo)tanc̃ꝫ nos extarēt.Nullos habent in cor
pore pilos p̃tercꝫ crines q̃s ꝓceros nigreſcēteſcꝫ ge
runt/& preſertim fœminę quę ꝓpterea ſunt tali lō⸗
go nigrocꝫ crine decore.Vultu nō multum ſpecioſi
ſunt q̃m latas facies tartarijs adſimilatas habēt/ nul
lus ſibi ſinūt in ſupercilicijs oculorꝛue palpebris ac

A v

rorpe toto(crinibus demptis) excrefcere villos/ ob
id quod habitos in corpore pilos quid beftiale bru
taleq; reputāt. Omnes tam viri q; mulieres siue me
ando/ siue currendo leues admodū atq; veloces ex
istunt:qm(vt frequenter experti fuimus) ipsę etiam
mulieres vnā aut duas pcurrere leucas nihili putāt/
& in hoc nos christicolas/multū pcellunt. Mirabili
ter ac vltra q; sit credibile natāt:multo quoq; meli╸
us fœminę q; masculi quod frequenti experimento
didicimus/cū ipsas ętiā fęminas omni prorsus sustē
tamine deficientes duas in ęquore leucas pernatare
pspeximus. Arma eoꝝ/ arcus sunt & sagitte/ quas
multū subtiliter fabricare norunt. Ferro metallisq;
alijs carent:sed pro ferro bestiarum pisciumue den
tibus suas sagittas armant/quas etiam(vt fortiores
existant) vna quoq; sepe pręurunt. Sagittarij sunt
certissimi.Ita vt quicquid voluerint iaculis suis feri╸
ant:nonnullisq; in locis mulieres quoq; optimę sa╸
gittatrices extant. Alia etiā arma habent veluti lan
ceas pręacutasue sudes/necnō & clauas capita mi╸
rifice laborata habentes.Pugnare potissimū assueti
sunt aduersus suos alienigenę linguę confines con╸
tra q̃s nullis parcendo(nisi vt eos ad acriora tormē
ta referuent)multū crudeliter dimicant. Et cū in pre
lium pperant suas secum vxores(non belligeratu╸
ras/sed eoꝝ post eos necessaria perlaturas) ducunt
ob id cp sola ex eis mulier tergo sibi plus imponere

poſſit/& deinde.xxx.vel.xl.ve leucis ſubuehere(p
ut ipſi ſepe vidimus)q̃ vir(etiam validus) a terra le
uare queat. Nulla belli capita/ nulloſue p̃ſectos ha
bēt/quinimo(cū eoꝝ quilibet ex ſe dominus extet)
nullo ſeruato ordine meant. Nulla regnandi domi
niuue ſuum extendendi/aut alterius inordinatę cu⸝
piditatis gratia pugnant: ſed veterem ſolum ob ini
miciciam in illis ab antiquo inſitam:cuiuſquidē ini⸝
micicię cauſam interrogati nullā aliā indicāt/ niſi vt
ſuorū mortes vendicent anteceſſoꝝ.Hæc gens ſua
in libertate viuens/ nulliꞇ obediens/ nec regē/ nec
dominū habet. Ad pręliū autē ſe potiſſimū animāt
& accingunt/cum eorū hoſtes ex eis quempiā aut
captiuum detinent aut interemerunt. Tunc em̄ eiuſ
dem captiui interemptiue conſanguineus ſenior q̃ſ
q̃ exurgens:exit cito in plateas & vicos paſſim cla
mitans inuitanſꞇ omnes & ſuadens vt cū eo in p̃⸝
lium conſanguinei ſui necem vindicaturi ꝓperent:
qui omnes cōpaſſione moti/mox ad pugnam ſe ac
cingunt atꞇ repēte in ſuos inimicos irruunt.Nulla
iura/nullamue iuſticiam ſeruant/malefactores ſuos
nequaꞇ puniunt: quinimo nec parentes ipſi/ par⸝
uulos ſuos edocent aut corripiūt. Mirabiliter eos
inter ſeſe conqueſtionari nonnunꞇ vidimus.Sim⸝
plices in loquela ſe oſtentāt/ verum callidi multum
atꞇ aſtuti ſunt.Perraro/ & ſummiſſa voce loquun
tur:eiſdē quibus vtimur accētibus vtentes.Suas vt

plurimu voces inter dentes & labra formātes: alijs
vtuntur vocabulis ꝙ̃ nos. Horū plurimę ſunt idio⸗
matum varietates/quoniā a cētenario leucarum in
centenariū diuerſitatem linguarum ſe mutuo nulla
tenus intelligētiū reperimus. Cōmeſſandi modum
valde barbarum retinent/nec quidem notatis man
ducāt horis/ ſed ſiue noĉte ſiue die: quotiens eden
di libido ſuadet. Solo manducantes accumbunt/&
nulla mantilia/nullaue gauſapa(cū lineamentis pan
niſꝗ alijs careant) habent. Epulas ſuas atꝗ cibaria
in vaſcula terrea quę ipſimet cōfingunt/ aut in me⸗
dias cucurbitarū teſtas ponūt. In retiaculis quibuſ⸗
dam magnis ex bombice factis & in aere ſuſpenſia
dormitant: qui modus ꝙ̃uis inſolitus & aſperior
ſortaſſis viderı queat/ego nihilominus talē dormi⸗
tandi modum ſuauem plurimum iudico. Etenim cū
in eiſdem eorum retiaculis mihi plerumꝗ dormitaſ
ſe contigerit/ in illis mihi metipſi melius ꝙ̃ in tape⸗
tibus quæ habebamus eſſe perſenſi. Corpore val⸗
de mundi ſunt & expoliti/ ex eo ꝗ ſeipſos frequē⸗
tiſſime lauant. Et cum egeſtum ire(quod ſalua di⸗
xerım reuerentia) coaĉti ſunt/omni conamıne nı⸗
tuntur/vt a nemine perſpici poſſint: qui quidem in
hoc quāto honeſti ſunt/tanto in dimittenda vrina
ſe imundos inuerecundoſꝗ/tam mares ꝙ̃ fœminę
præbent: cum ſiquidem illos nobıſcum loqnentes/
& coram politos ſuà impudiciſſime vtinam ſepius

eminxiſſe ·pſpeximus. Nullam legē/nullũ legitimũ
thori fœdus in ſuis cōnubijs obſeruāt:quinimo q̃tↄ
quot mulieres quiſ᷏ cōcupiſcit:tot habere & dein
illas qñcũᷗ volet(abſ᷏ hoc ᷗ id ⱷ iniuria aut opↄ
probrio habeāt) repudiare pōt. Et in hac re vti᷏ tã
viri ᷗ mulieres eadē libertate fruunt̃. Zœloſi parũ
libidinoſi vero plurimũ extant:magiſ᷏ fœminꝗ ᷗ
maſculi:quaꝛ artificia vt inſatiabili ſuꝗ ſatiſſaciant
libidini hic honeſtatis gratia ſubticenda cenſuimus
Eꝗ ipſꝗ in generandis paruulis fœcundꝗ admodum
ſunt:neᷗ dũ grauidꝗ effectꝗ ſunt pœnas aut laboↄ
res euitant. Leuiſſimo minimoᷗ dolore pariũt. Ita
vt in craſtinũ alacres ſanatꝗᷗ vbiᷗ ambulent:prꝗↄ
ſertimᷗ poſt partũ in flumē quopiã ſeſe ablutũ va
dunt/tumᷗ ſanꝗ mundatꝗᷗ inde(veluti piſcis) ap
parēt. Crudelitati autē ac odio maligno adeo dediↄ
tꝗ ſunt:vt ſi illas ſui forſitã exacerbauerint viri/ſubi
to certũ quoddã efficiũt maleficiũ:cũ quo ꝑ ingenti
ira ⱶprios fœtus in ⱶprijs vteris necāt abortiũtᷗ
deinde:cuius rei occaſiōe infiniti eoꝛ paruuli ꝑeũt.
Venuſto/& eleganti ⱶportione cōpacto/corpore
ſunt. Ita vt in illis quic᷏ deforme nullo inſpici moↄ
do poſſit. Et q̃uis diſnude ambulent inter fœmina
tamen eaꝛ/pudibunda ſic honeſte repoſita ſunt/vt
nullatenus videri queant/ꝑterquã regiũcula illa an
terior/ quã verecũdiore vocabulo pectuſculũ imũ
vocamus quod & in illis vti᷏ nō aliter ᷗ honeſte

natura ipfa vidēdum reliquit. Sed & hoc nec quidē
curant qm̄(vt paucis expediā)nō magis in ſuoꝛ vi
ſione pudendoꝛ mouenī/ꝗ nos in oris noſtri/ aut
vultus oſtētatione. Admirandā per valde rem du/
cerent mulierē in eis mamillas/ pulpas velaxas/ aut
vētrem rugatū ob nimiū partū habentē/ cū omnes
equę integrę ac ſolide poſt partū ſemp appareāt:ac
ſi nunꝗ peperiſſent. Hee quidē ſe noſtri cupiētiſſi⸗
mas eſſe monſtrabant. Neminem in hac gente legē
aliquā obſeruare vidimus:nec quidē iudei aut mau
ri nuncupari ſolide queunt:cum ipſis gentilibus aut
paganis multo deteriores ſint. Etenim nō perſenſi⸗
mus ꝗ ſacrificia vlla faciant/aut ꝗ loca orationiſue
domos aliquas habeant:hoꝛ vitā(quę omnino vo
luptuoſa eſt) Epycuriam exiſtimo. Illorum habita⸗
tiones ſingulis ipſis ſunt cōmunes/ ipſęꝗ illorū do
mus campanarum inſtar cōſtructe ſunt firmiter ex
magnis arboribus ſolidate/ palmarum folijs deſu⸗
per contectę/& aduerſus vētos & tempeſtates tu⸗
tiſſime/ nonnulliſꝗ in locis tam magnę/ vt in illa⸗
rum vnica ſexcentas eſſe perſonas inuenerimus. In
ter quas octo populoſiſſimas eſſe comperimus: ſic
vt in eis eſſent habitarentꝗ pariter animarū decem
millia. Octennio quolibet/ aut ſeptennio/ ſuas ſe⸗
des habitationeſue transferunt/ qui eius rei cauſam
interrogati/ naturale reſponſum dederunt/ dicen⸗
tes ꝗ phœbi vehemētis eſtus occaſionę hoc facerēt

ob id q̃ ex illorum longiore in eodem loco residen
tia aer infectus corruptusq̃ redderetur/ quæ res in
eorum corporibus varias caufaret egritudines/que
quidem eorum ratio non male fumpta/ nobis vifa
eft. Eorum diuitiæ funt variorum colorum anium
plumę/ aut in modum lapilloru illorum/ quos vul-
gariter pater nofter vocitamus lamine fiue calculi/
quos ex pifciu offibus lapillisve viridibus aut can-
didis faciunt: & hos ornatus gratia fibi ad genas la
bia vel aures fufpēdūt. Alia quoq̃ fimilia futilia &
leuia pro diuitijs habent/ quæ nos omnino parui
pendebamus. Commutationibus aut mercimonijs
in vendendo/ aut emendo nullis vtuntur / quibus
fatis eft quod natura fponte fua propinat Aurum
vniones iocalia cæteraq̃ fimilia/ quæ in hac Europa pro diuitijs habemus nihil extimãt/immo penitus fpernunt/nec habere curant. In dando fic natu-
raliter liberaliffimi funt/ vt nihil quod ab eis expe-
tatur abnegent. Et quemadmodum in dando li-
berales funt fic in petendo & accipiendo cupidiffi-
mi poftq̃ fe cuiquam amicos exhibuerint. Maxi-
mum potiffimumq̃ amicicię fue fignum in hoc per
hibent/ q̃ tam vxores q̃ filias proprias amicis fuis
pro libito habendas offerunt/in qua re parens vter
q̃ fe longe honoratũ iri exiftimat cum natã eius(&
fi virginem)ad concubitũ fuum quifpiam dignatur
& abducit:& in hoc fuam inter fe amiciciã potiffi-

mum conciliant. Varijs in eorꝛ deceſſu multiꝗ mo
dis exequijs vtunt̃. Porro ſuos nõnulli defũctos in
humo cũ aqua ſepeliunt & inhumant illis ad caput
victualia ponẽtes quibus eos poſce veſci & alimen
tari putãt:nullũ deinde ᵖpter eos aliũ planctũ/ aut
alias cerimoniás efficiẽtes. Alij q̄buſdã in locis barꝰ
bariſſimo atꝗ inhumaniſſimo ſepeliẽdi vtunt̃ moꝰ
do. Quippe cũ eorꝛ quẽpiam mortis momẽto ᵖxi
mũ autumant:illũ eius ᵖpinquiores/in ſiluã ingenꝰ
tem quandã deferunt: vbi eũ in bombiceis retiacuꝰ
lis illis in quibus dormitant impoſitũ & recubantẽ
ad duas arbores in aera ſuſpendũt/ ac poſtmodum
ductis circa eũ ſic ſuſpenſum vna tota die choreis
(irruẽte interim nocte)ei aquã/victũcꝗ aliũ/ ex quo
quattuor aut circit̃ dies viuere q̄at ad caput appoꝰ
nũt:& deinde(ſic inibi ſolo pẽdente relicto)ad ſuas
habitatiões redeũt:quibus ita pactis ſi iſdẽ ᵉgrotus
poſtea mãducet & bibat/ ac inde ad cõualeſcentiã
ſanitatẽcꝗ redeat/ & ad habitationẽ ᵖpriã remeet
illũ eius affines ac ᵖpinqui/cũ maximis ſuſcipiũt ce
rimonijs. At ᵖpauci ſunt qui tã grãde ᵖtereant peri
culum/cũ eos ibidẽ nemo poſtea viſitet: qui ſi tunc
inibi forſitan decedũt nullã aliã habẽt poſtea ſepul
turam. Alios quocꝗ cõplures barbaros habẽt ritus
quos euitande ᵖlixitatis hic omittimus gratia. Diꝰ
uerſis varijſcꝗ medicaminibus ĩ ſuis morbis & ᵉgri
tudinibus vtunt̃/q̄ ſic a noſtris diſcrepãt & diſcon

ueniunt. vt mirarenť/ haud parũ qualiter inde quis
euadere poſſet. Nempe(vt frequẽti didicimus expe
ríentia)cũ eoꝛ quẽpiã febricitare contigerit/hora q̃
febris eũ aſperius inqetat iṗm in frigentiſſimã aquã
immergũt & balneant/ poſtmodũcꝫ ꝓ duas horas
circa ignẽ validum(donec plurimũ caleſcat)currere
& recurrere cogũt:& poſtremo ad dormiendũ de
ferũt quoquidẽ medicamẽto cõplures eoꝛ ſanitati
reſtitui vidimus. Dietis etiã(qbus tribus q̃ttuorve
diebus abſcꝫ cibo & potu ꝑſiſtunt)frequentiſſimis
vtunť. Sanguinẽ quocꝫ ſibi ꝑſepe cõminuũt nõ in
brachíjs(ſalua ala)ſed ĩ lumbis & tibiaꝛ pulpis. Se
ipſos etiã ad vomĩtũ cũ certis herbis quas in ore de
ferunt medicaminis gr̃a plerũcꝫ ꝓuocãt/ & multis
alíjs remedíjs antidotiſcꝫ vtunť/q̃ longũ dinumera
re foret.Multo ſanguine mⁱſtocꝫ flegmatico humo
re habundãt cibarioꝛ ſuoꝛ occaſione/ q̃ ex radici
bus/fructibus/herbis/varíjſcꝫ piſcibus faciũt.Om
ni farris granorũcꝫ alioꝛ ſemine carẽt.Cõmunisve
ro eoꝛ paſtus ſiue victus ſiue arborea radix quedã
eſt/quã ĩ farrinã ſatis bonã cõminuũt/& hãc radicẽ
qdã eoꝛ iucha/alíj chambi/ alíj ẏo ignami vocitãt
Alíjs carnibus/ ꝑterq̃ hoĩm ꝑ raro veſcunt in qui
buſquidẽ hoĩm carnibus vorãdis ſic inhumani ſũt
& inmanſueti:vt in hoc oẽm ferale/omnẽue beſtia
lem modũ ſupent/ oẽs eĩ hoſtes ſuos q̃s aut peri
mũt aut captos detinẽt tã viros q̃ ſẽminas indiſtin

b

cte cũ ea feritate deglutiũt vt nihil ferũ/ nihilve bru
tum magis dici vel inſpici queat/quoſquidẽ ſic eſe/
ros ĩmaneſcʒ fore/varijs in locis mihi frequẽtius cõ
tigit aſpexiſſe/mirãtibus illis cʒ inimicos nr̃os ſic q̃
cʒ nequacʒ mãducaremus. Et hoc ꝑ certo maieſtas
veſtra regia teneat. Eoꝝ cõſuetudines(quas pluri/
mas habent)ſic barbare ſunt/vt hic nunc ſufficien/
ter ſatis enarrari nõ valeant. Et qm̃ in meis hiſce bis
geminis nauigationibus/ tam varia diuerſacʒ/ac tã
a noſtris rebus & modis differentia perſpexi. Idcir
co libellũ quẽpiam(quẽ quattor dietas ſiue quattu/
or nauigationes appello)conſcribere paraui cõſcri/
pſicʒ/in quo maiorẽ reꝝ a me viſaꝝ partẽ diſtincte
ſatis/iuxta ingenioli mei tenuitatẽ collegi. Verũta/
men nõ adhuc publicaui. In illo ẙo qm̃ omnia par/
ticulariter magis ac ſingillatim tangenť/idcirco vni
uerſalia hic ſolummodo proſequens: ad nauigatio/
nem noſtram priorẽ perficiendam a qua pauliſper
digreſſus fueram iam redeo.

IN HOC NAVIGII NOSTRI PRIMOR:
dio notabilis cõmoditatis res non vidimus/ idcirco
(vt opinor)cʒ eoꝝ linguã nõ capiebamus/ prętercʒ
nõnullã auri denotantiã/qd' nõnulla indicia in tellu
re illa eſſe mõſtrabant. Heccine ẙo tellus q̃ ad ſui ſi
tũ poſitionẽcʒ tã bona eſt:vt vix dari melior queat.
Cõcordauimus aũt vt illã derelinquẽtes lõgius na/
uigationem ꝑduceremus. Qua vnanimitate ſuſce/

pta/nos dehinc aridã ipſam collateralit̃ ſemp̃ ſectã
tes/necnõ gyros mĩtos ſcalaſc̃p plurès circũeuntes
& interim cũ mĩtis varijſc̃p locorꝣ illorꝣ incolis cõ
ferentiã habentes/tandẽ certos poſt aliĩqt dies por
tui cuidã applicuimus/in q̃ nos grandi a periculo al
titono ſpiritui cõplacuit eripe. Huius ẽ modi por
tũ c̃pprimũ introgreſſi fuimus populationẽ vnã eo
rũ hoc eſt pagũ aut villã ſup̃ aquas(vt Venetiẹ)pó
ſitã cõperimus /in qua ingentes.xx.edes aut circiter
erant/in modũ campanarũ(vt prẹtactũ eſt) effecte
atc̃p ſup̃ ligneis vallis ſolidis & fortibus firmiter fũ
date/prẹ quarũ porticibus leuaticij põtes porrecti
erant:per quos ab altera ad alteram tanc̃p per com
pactiſſimã ſtratam tranſitus erat. Igitur huiuſmodi
populationis incolẹ c̃pprimum nos intuiti ſunt ma
gno ͵ppter nos timore affecti ſunt/ c̃p ob rem ſuos
confeſtim pontes omnes cõtra nos eleuauerunt/&
ſeſe deinde in ſuis domibus abdiderũt. Quam rem
proſpectantibus nobis/ & haud parum admiran
tibus/ecce duodecim eorum lintres vel circiter ſin
gulas ex ſolo arboris candice cauatas(quo nauium
genere vtunt̃) ad nos interim per ẹquor aduentare
conſpeximus/quorꝣ naucleri effigiem noſtrã habi
tũc̃p mirantes ac ſeſe circũ nos vndic̃p circumferen
tes/nos eminus aſpiciebãt. Quos nos quoc̃p ex ad
uerſo proſpicientes/plurima eis amiciciẹ ſigna dedi
mus/ quibus eos/ vt ad nos in trepidi accederent/

exhortabamur/qd̃ tñ efficere contēpſerũt. Quā rē
nobis p̃cipiētibus mox ad eos remigare incœpimus
q̃ nequacꝫ nos p̃ſtolati ſunt:quinimo oēs cōfeſtim
in terram fugerũt datis nobis interim ſignis vt illos
pauliſper expectaremus.Ipſi eñ ex templo reuerſu
ri forent. Tumcꝫ in montē quendā ꝓperauerũt/a q̃
eductis bis octo iuuēculis & in lintribus ſuis p̃fatis
vna ſecũ aſſumptis mox ỹſus nos regreſſi ſunt. Et
poſt hæc ex iuuēculis ipſis q̃ttuor/in ſingulis nauiũ
noſtrarꝫ poſuerũt:quē faciēdi modũ nos haud parꝫ
admirati tũc fuimus/ꝓput vr̃a ſatis ꝓpendere poteſt
maieſtas. Cęterũcꝫ cũ lintribus ſuis p̃miſſis inť nos
naueſcꝫ nr̃as cōmixti ſunt/& nobiſcũ ſic pacifice lo
cuti ſũt/vt illos amicos nr̃os fideliſſimos eſſe repu﹣
taremus.Interea ỹo ecce q̃cꝫ ex domibus eorꝫ ꝓme
moratis gens nō modica ꝑ mare natitans aduētare
cœpit:quibus ita adueniētibus & nauibus nr̃is iam
appropinq̃re incipientibus/nec tñ ꝓinde mali qcꝫ
adhuc ſuſpicaremur:rurſum ad earũdē domorꝫ eo﹣
rum fores/vetulas nōnullas cōſpeximus q̃ immani
ter vociferātes & cœlũ magnis clamoribus implen
tes ſibimet/in magne anxietatis in indiciũ ꝓprios
euellebāt capillos: q̃ res magnā mali ſuſpectionem
nobis tũc attulit.Tumcꝫ ſubito factũ eſt vt iuuēcu﹣
le ille quas in nr̃is impoſuerũt nauibus mox in ma﹣
re ꝓſilirent/ac illi qui in lintribus erant ſeſe a nobis
elongantes mox contra nos arcus ſuos intenderēt:

nosqʒ duriſſime ſagittarẽt. Qui vero a domibus p̱
mare natantes adueniebãt ſinguli latentes in vndis
lanceas ferebant/ex quibus eoꝝ ꝓditionẽ cognoui
mus.Et tũ nõ ſolũ noſmet magnanimiter defende¬
re/ verũ etiã illos grauiter offendere inçepimus. Ita
vt plures eoꝝ faſellos cũ ſtrage eoꝝ nõ parua p̄fre
gerimus/& pœnitus in ponto ſubmerſerimus: pro
pter qd̕ʼreliquis faſelis ſuis cũ damno eoꝝ maximo
relictis/p̱ mare natantes omnes in terrã fugerunt in
ter emptis ex eis.xx. vel circiter/ vulneratis v̓o plu
ribus:& ex noſtris v̓o quincqʒ dumtaxat leſis/q̃ om
nes ex dei gratia incolumitati reſtituti ſunt. Comp̄
hendimus autẽ & tunc ex p̄tactis iuuenculis duas¬
& viros tres/ac dehinc domos eoꝝ viſitauimus &
in illas introiuimus/ verũ in eis quicq̃ʒ(niſi vetulas
duas & ꝏgrotantẽ virũ vnicũ)nõ inuenimus/q̃ſqui
dem eoꝝ domos igni ſuccendere nõ voluimus: ob
id cꝗ cõſcientiꝫ ſcrupulũ hoc ipſum eſſe formidaba¬
mus.Poſt hꝫc autẽ ad naues nr̃as cũ prꝫtactis captú
uis ꝗncꝗ remeauimus/ & eoſdẽ captiuos/p̄tercꝗ iu
uenculas ipſas in compedibus ferreis alligauimus.
Eedem v̓o iuuẽcule captiuorũcꝗ virorũ vnus ſuper
uenienti nocte a nobis ſubtiliſſime euaſerũt: his ita
cꝗ pactis/ſequẽti die cõcordauimus/vt relicto por¬
tu illo longius ſcd̕m collem ꝓcederemus/p̱cuſſiſcꝗ
lxxx. fere leucis gentẽ aliã quandam comperimus
lingua & cõuerſatione ꝑꝫnitus a priore diuerſam.

Conuenimusc̃q vt classem inibi nostrã anchorare
mus & deinde in terrã ipsam/cũ nauiculis nr̃is acce
deremus. Vidimus autẽ tũc ad littus i plaga gentiũ
turbã.iiij.M.psonarũ vel circiter existere/q̃ cũ nos
appropriare persenserũt nequac̃q nos p̃stolati sunt
quinimo(cunctis q̃ habebãt relictis) oẽs in siluas et
nemora diffugerunt. Tum v̊o in terrã psilientes/&
viã vnã in siluas tendentẽ/c̃q̃tus est baliste iactus/p
ambulantes/mox tentoria plura inuenimus que ibi
dem ad piscandũ gens illa tetenderat: & in illis co-
piosos ad de coquendas epulas suas ignes accende
rat/ac psecto bestias ac p̃es variarz specierũ pisces
iam assabat. Vidimus autẽ inibi certũ assari animal
quod erat(demptis alis quibus carebat) serpenti si-
millimũ tamc̃q brutũ ac siluestre apparebat/ vt eius
nõ modicũ miraremur feritatẽ. Nobis vero per eadem tentoria longius pgredientibus/ plurimos hu
iuscemodi serpẽtes viuos inuenimus/qui ligatis pe
dibus ora quoc̃q finibus ligata/ne eadẽ aperire pos
sent/habebãt/put de canibus aut feris alijs ne mor
dere queant effici solet. Aspectũ tam ferũ eadem p̃
se ferũt animalia vt nos illa venenosa putantes nul
latenus auderemus cõtingere. Capreolis in magni
tudine:brachio vero cũ medio/in lõgitudine equa-
lia sunt.Pedes longos materialesc̃q multum ac forti
bus vngulis armatos/necnõ & discholorẽ pellẽ di-
uersissimã habẽt/nostrũc̃q ac faciẽ veri serpẽtis ge-

ftant/a quoꝝ naribus vſcꝫ ad extremã caudam ſe⸗
ta quedã per tergũ ſic protendiꝉ vt animalia illa ve⸗
ros ſerpentes eſſe iudicaremus/ & nihilominus eis
gens ꝑfata veſciꝉ.Pane ſuũ gens eadem ex piſcibus
quos in mari piſcanꝉ efficiunt. Primũ eꝿ piſciculos
ipſos inſeruenti aqua aliquantiſper excoqnũt. De⸗
inde vero contundunt & cõpiſtant/& in panes cõ
glutinant quos ſup prunas inſup torrent & tandẽ
inde poſtea mãducant/hoſquidẽ panes ꝓbantes cꝫ
bonos eſſe reperimus. Alia quocꝫ cꝫmulta eſculẽta
cibariacꝫ tam in fructibus cꝫ in varijs radicibus reti
nent ꝙ longũ enumerare foret.Cum autẽ a ſiluis ad
ꝙs auſugerãt nõ redirẽt nihil de rebus eoꝝ (vt am⸗
plius de nobis ſecuri fierẽt)auferre voluimus:quin⸗
imo in eiſdẽ eoꝝ tentorijs ꝓmſta de reculis nꝵris/in
locis ꝙ ꝑpendere poſſent/derelinquentes ad naues
nꝵras ſub noctẽ repediauimus. Sequẽti ỿo die cũ ex
oriri titan inciperet/infinitã in littore gentẽ exiſtere
percepimus/ad ꝙs in terrã tũc acceſſimus. Et cꝫuis
ſe noſtri timidos oſtẽderẽt ſeipſos/ tñ inter nos per
miſcuerũt/& nobiſcũ practicare ac cõuerſari cũ ſe⸗
curitate ceperũt/ amicos nꝵros ſe plurimũ fore perſi
mulantes/inſinuãteſcꝫ illic habitatiões eoꝝ nõ eſſe
verũ cp piſcandi gꝵa aduenerãt. Et idcirco rogitan⸗
tes/ vt ad eoꝝ pagos cũ eis accederemus:ipſi etẽ
nos tancꝫ amicos recipe vellẽt/& hãc quidẽ de no⸗
bis cõceperãt amiciciã/captiuoꝝ ilioꝝ duoꝝ(quos

tenebamus)occaſione/qui eoꝛ inimici erant. Viſa
autē eoꝛ magna rogādi importunitate cōcordaui⸗
mus.xxiij.ex nobis cū illis in bono apparatu cū ſta
bili mente (ſi cogeret neceſſitas) oēs ſtrēnue mori.
Cum itacꝫ nobiſcū p̄ tres extitiſſent dies & tres cū
eis p̄ plagā terrācꝫ illā exceſſiſſemus leucas/ ad pa⸗
gū vnū/nouē dūtaxat domoꝛ venimus: vbi cū tot
tācꝫ barbaris cerimonijs ab eis ſuſcepti fuimus/ vt
ſcribere penna nō valeat:vtputa cū choreis & cāti⸗
cis ac planctibus hilaritate & leticia mixtis/necnon
cū ferculis cibarijſcꝫ multis.Et ibidem nocte illa re⸗
quieuimus/ vbi ꝓprias vxores ſuas nobis cū omni
ꝓdigalitate obtulerunt/q̄ quidē nos ſic importune
ſolicitabant vt vix eiſdē reſiſtere ſufficeremus:poſt
cꝫ aūt illic nocte vna cū media die p̄ſtitimus/ ingēs
admirabiliſcꝫ populus abſcꝫ cūctatione ſtuporecꝫ
ad nos inſpiciēdos aduenit: quoꝛ ſeniores nos q̄cꝫ
rogabāt/vt ſecū ad alios eoꝛ pagos(qui longius in
terra erāt)cōmearemus qd̄ & quidē eis annuimns.
Hic dictu facile nō eſt q̄tos ipſi nobis impēderunt
honores.Fuimus autē apud q̄multas eoꝛ popula
tiones/p̄ integros nouē dies cū ipſis euntes/ ob qd̄
nobis noſtri q̄ in nauibus remāſerāt retulerūt ſocij
ſe idcirco plerūcꝫ in anxietate timorecꝫ nō minimo
extitiſſe.Nobis autē bis nouē leucis aut circit́ in eo
rū terra exiſtentibus/ad naues nr̄as repedare ꝓpo
ſuimus.Et quidē nr̄o in regreſſu tam copioſa ex eis

viroꝝ ac mulierū multitudo accurrit/ qui nos vſq̃
ad mare ‚pſecuti ſunt: vt hoc ipſum mirabile foret.
Cūq̃ nr̃i quempiā ex itinere fatigatū iri cōtingeret:
ipſi nos ſubleuabant/ & in ſuis retiaculis in quibus
dormitant ſtudioſiſſime ſubuehebāt. In tranſitu q̃⸗
q̃ flumiuū(quę apud eos plurima ſunt & maxima)
ſic nos cum ſuis artificijs ſecure trāſmittebāt:vt nul
la vſq̃ pericula ptimeſceremus. Plurimi etiam eoꝝ
nos comitabanꝉ rerū ſuaꝛ onuſti/quas nobis dede
rāt/illas in retiaculis illis quibus dormiūt vectantes
plumaria videlicet p̃ditia/necnō arcus mltos/ ſagit
taſq̃ multas/ac infinitos diuerſorū coloꝛ pſitacos.
Alij quoq̃ cōplures ſupellectilem ſuā totā ferentes
aialia:etiā ſua ſecū ducebāt. Et quiddā admirabilē
dicā:q̃ is fortunatū ſe fœliceq̃ putabat q in trāſme
andis aquis nos ī collo dorſoue ſuo trāſuectare po
terat. Quāprimū autē ad mare ptigimus & faſelos
noſtros cōſcēdere voluimus/ in ipſo faſelorū nr̃oꝛ
aſcenſu:tāta ipſorū nos cōmiꝗantiū/& nobiſcū aſcē
dere cōcertantiū/ac naues nr̃as videre cōcupiſcen⸗
tium preſſura fuit: vt noſtri idē faſeli pene p̃ ponde
re ſubmergerēꝉ.In ipſis aūt nr̃is eiſdē faſelis recepi
mus ex eis nobiſcū quotꝗt potuimus:ac eos ad na⸗
ues noſtras vſq̃ pduximus.Tanti etiā illorū p ma⸗
re natantes/ & vna nos cōcomitātes aduenerūt: vt
tot aduētare moleſtiuſcule ferremus/ cū ſiqdē plu⸗
res q̃ mille in nr̃as naues/ licet nudi & inermes in⸗

c

troiuiſſent/apparatum artificiũ{que} noſtrũ/necnõ &
nauiũ ipſarũ magnitudinẽ mirãtes. Aſt tũc quiddã
riſu dignũ accidit. Nã cũ machinaꝛ/tormentorũ{que}
bellicoꝛ noſtroꝛ quędã exonerare cõcuperemus:
& ‚ppter hoc(impoſito igne) machinę ipſę horridiſ
ſime tonuiſſent/pars illoꝛ maxima(audito huiuſce
modi tonitruo)ſeſe in mare natitans ꝑcipitauit:ve⸗
luti ſolite ſunt rane in ripa ſidentes: q̃ ſi fortaſſis tu⸗
multuoſum quic{que} audiũt/ſeſe in ‚pfundũ luti latita
turę ĩmergũt/ quẽadmodũ & gẽs illa tunc fęcerunt
illic{que} eoꝛ qui ad naues aufugerãt:ſic tũc pterriti fue
runt:vt nos facti noſtri noſmet rephẽderemus. Ve⸗
rũ illos mox ſecuros eſſe fęcimus:nec amplius ſtupi
dos eſſe ꝑmiſimus/ inſinuantes eis {quod} cũ talibus ar⸗
mis hoſtes nꝫos perimeremus. Poſt{que} autẽ illos illa
tota die in nauibus nꝫis feſtiuę tractauimus/ipſos a
nobis abituros eſſe monuimus: q̃m ſequenti nocte
nos ab hĩc abſcedere cupiebamus. Quo audito/iꝑ̃
cũ ſũma amicicia beneuolẽtia{que} mox a nobis egreſ
ſi ſunt. In hac gẽte eoꝛ̃{que} terra q̃multos eoꝛ̃ ritus
vidi cognouiq̃ in quibus hic diutins ĩmorari nõ cu
pio. Cum poſtea noſſe veſtra queat maieſtas q̃liter
in quauis nauigationũ haꝛ mearũ magis admiran⸗
da annotatu{que} digniora cõſcripſerim ac in libellum
vnũ ſtilo geographico collegerẽ quẽ libellũ q̃ttuor
dietas intitulaui & in q̃ ſingula particulariꝰ & minu
tim notaui: ſed hactenus a me nõ emiſi ob id {quod} illũ

adhuc reuifere collationareĉ mihi neceſſe eſt. Ter⸗
ra illa gente multa populoſa eſt ac multis diuerſiſĉ
animalibus & noſtris pauciſſime ſimilibus vndiĉ
denſiſſima. Demptis leonibus/vrſis/ceruis/ſuibus/
capreoliſĉ/& dāmis/q̄ & quidē deformitatē quā⸗
dā a noſtris retinēt/ęquis/ac mulis/aſiniſĉ/ & cani
bus/ac omni minuto pecore(vt ſūt oues & ſimilia)
necnō & vaccinis armētis pęnitus carēt/verūtamē
alijs q̄plurimis variorꝫ generū aīalibus(quę nō fa⸗
cile dixerim)habundantes ſunt:ſed tñ oīa ſilueſtria
ſunt:quibus in ſuis agēdis minime vtunt. Quid plu
ra:Hij tot tantiſĉ diuerſorꝫ modorū ac colorꝫ pen
narūĉ alitibus fecūdi ſunt: vt id ſit viſu enarratuĉ
mirabile:regio ſiquidē illa multū amena fructiferaꝫ
ĉ eſt/ ſiluis ac nemoribus maximis plena/ q̄ oī tꝑe
virēt/nec eorꝫ vnĉ folia fluunt. Fructus etiā innu⸗
merabiles & noſtris omnino diſſimiles habēt. Hęc
cine tellus in torrida zona ſita eſt directe ſub paral⸗
lello qui cancri tropicum deſcribit vñ polus orizon
tis eiuſdē ſe.xxiij. gradibus eleuat in fine climatis ſe
cundi. Nobis autē inibi exiſtentibus nos cōtēplatū
populus multus aduenit/ effigiem albedinemĉ no
ſtram mirantes:quibus vnde veniremus ſciſcitanti
bus:e cœlo inuiſcende terre gratia nos deſcendiſſe
reſpondimus/quod & vtiĉ ipſi credebāt:in hac tel
lure baptiſteria fonteſue ſacros plures inſtituimus:
in quibus eorum infiniti ſeipſos baptiſari fœcerūt

se eorũ lingua charaibi/hoc est magnę sapientię vi
ros vocantes. Et ꝓuincia ipsa Parias ab ipsis nũcu
pata est. Postea autẽ portũ illũ terrãcꝗ derelinquen
tes ac scdm collẽ transnauigantes & terrã ipsam vi
su semp sequẽtes. D ccc.lxx.leũcas a portu illo per
currimus: faciẽtes gyros circuitusꝗ interim multos
& cum gentibus multis cõuersantes practicantescꝗ
Vbi in pleriscꝗ locis aurum(sed nõ in grandi copia)
emimus/cũ nobis terras illas reperire & si in eis au
rum foret: tunc sufficeret cognoscere. Et quia tunc
xiij.iã mensibus in nauigatione nostra pstiteramus
& naualia nostra/apparatuscꝗ nostri/toti pęne cõ
sumpti erãt hoiescꝗ labore pfracti. Communẽ inter
nos de restaurãdis nauiculis nostris(quę aquã vndi
cꝗ recipiebãt)& repetunda hyspania/iniuimus con
cordiã/in quã dum psisteremus vnanimitatę/ ꝓpe
portum vnũ eramus totius orbis optimũ: in quẽ cũ
nauibus nostris introeuntes/gentẽ ibidẽ infinitã in
uenimus/quę nos cum magna suscepit amicicia: in
terra autẽ illa nauiculã vnã cũ reliquis nauiculis no
stris ac dolijs/nouã fabricauimus: ipsascꝗ machinas
nostras ac tormẽta bellica/quę in aquis vndicꝗ pe
ne peribãt: in terrã suscepimus/ nostrascꝗ naues ab
eis exonerauimus: & post hęc in terrã traximus: &
refecimus correximuscꝗ & penitus repauimus. In ꝗ
re eiusdẽ telluris incole: nõ paruũ nobis adiuuamẽ
exhibuere: quinimmo nobis de suis victualibus ex

affectu largiti sponte sua fuere/propter quod inibi perpauca de nostris cõsumpsimus: quãquidē rē ingenti ,p beneplacito duximus: cum satis tenuia tũc teneremus: cum quibus hyspaniã nostrã nõ(nisi indigentes)repetere potuissemus. In portu autem illo xxxvij. diebus pstitimus: frequētius ad populationes eorꝛ cum eis euntes: vbi singuli nobis nõ paruũ exhibebant honorē. Nobis autē portũ eundē exire & nauigationē nostrã reflectere concupiscentibus conquesti sunt illi gentē quandã valde ferocē & eis infestã existere: qui cęrto anni tempore ꝑ viã maris in ipsam eorũ terrã ꝑ insidias ingressi/ nunc ꝓditorie/nunc ꝑ vim q̃multos eorum interimerent/mãducarentcꝗ deinde. Alios ꝟo in suã terrã suascꝗ domos captiuatos duceret/cõtra quos ipsi se vix defē dere possent/ nobis insinuantes gentē illã quãdã in habitare insulã q̃ in mari leucis centũ aut circiꝉ eratꝰ Quã rem ipsi nobis cũ tãto affectu ac querimonia cõmemorauerũt: vt eis ex condolentia magna crederemus/ ꝓmitteremuscꝗ vt de tantis eos vindicaremus iniurijs/ꝓpter qd̄ illi letantes nõ parũ effecti sese nobiscũ vēturos sꝑõte sua ꝓpria obtulerũt: qd̄ plures ob causas acceptare recusauimus/ demptis septē/quos data cõditione recepimus: vt soli in suis lintribus in ꝓpria remearēt/ qm̄ reducendorũ eorũ curã suscipe nequacꝗ intendebamus/cui conditioni ipsi q̃gratãter acquieuerunt. Et ita illos amicos no

ſtros plurimũ effectos derelinquẽtes/ab eis abſceſ⸗
ſimus.Reſtauratis autẽ reparatiſcʒ naualibus nr̃is/
ſeptẽ p̱ gyrũ maris(vẽto inter grecũ:& leuantẽ nos
ducẽte)nauigauimus dies. Poſt q̃s plurimis obuia⸗
uimus inſulis quarũ quidẽ alię habitę/alię ꝟo diſcre
tę erãt.Harũ igit̃ vni tandẽ appropinquãtes & na⸗
ues noſtras inibi ſiſtere faciẽtes/vidimus ibidem c̃ʒ
maximũ gentis aceruũ:qui inſulã illam Ity nũcupa⸗
rẽt/quibus ꝑſpectis/ & nauiculis phaſeliſcʒ nr̃is vi
ris validis/& machinis tribus/ſtipatis/ terrę eidẽ vi
cinius appropinquantes.iiij.C.viros cũ mulieribus
c̃ʒmĺtis iuxta littus eſſe cõſpeximus:q̃(vt de priori
bus habitũ eſt)oẽs nudi meãtes/corpe ſtrẽnuo erãt
necnõ bellicoſi plurimũ/validicʒ apparebãt/cũ ſiq⸗
dem oẽs armis ſuis/arcubus videlicet & ſagittis/lã
ceiſcʒ armati eſſent/quorᴇ quo cʒ cõplures parmas
etiã/quadrataue ſcuta gerebãt/ quibus ſic oportu⸗
ne ſeſe p̃muniebãt/vt eos in iaculandis ſagittis ſuis
in aliquo nõ impedirent.Cũcʒ in phaſelis nr̃is terrę
ipſi c̃ʒtus eſt ſagittę volatus appropiaſſemus/ oẽs
citius in mare ꝓſilierunt/& infinitis emiſſis ſagittis
ſeſe cõtra nos ſtrẽnue(ne in terrã deſcendere poſſe
mus) defendere occeperũt. Omnes vero p̱ corpus
diuerſis coloribus depicti:& varijs volucrũ pennis
ornati erant/ q̃s hij qui nobiſcũ venerãt aſpicientes
illos ad preliandũ paratos eſſe/ q̃tienſcũcʒ ſic picti:
aut auium plumis ornati ſunt:nobis inſinuauerunt⸗

Intantũ aũt introitũ terrę nobis impedierũt vt faxi=
uomas machinas nr̃as in eos coacti fuerimus emit=
tere/quaꝝ auditu tumultu/impétuꞇ̃ vifo/necnon
ex eis plerifꞇ̃ in terram mortuis decidiſſe ꝓſpectis
oẽs in terrã feſe receperunt. Tumꞇ̃ facto inter nos
cõſilio.xlij.de nobis ĩ terrã poſt eos cõcordauimus
exilire/& aduerſus eos magno aĩo pugnare/qd̃ &
quidẽ fecimus.Nã tũ aduerſum illos in terrã cũ ar=
mis nr̃is ꝓſiluimus/cõtraꞇ̃ illi ſic feſe nobis oppo=
ſuer̃t/vt duabus ferme horis cõtinuũ inuicẽ geſſeri
mus bellũ/ꝓter id ꝗ de eis magnã faceremus victo
riã/dẽptis eoꝝ ꝑpaucis/ꝗs baliſtarij colubrinarijꞇ̃
noſtri/ fuis interemerũt telis: qd̃ idcirco ita effectũ
eſt/quia feipſos a nobis ac lãceis enſibuſꞇ̃ nr̃is/ſub
tiliter ſubtrahebât. Verũtñ tãta demũ in eos incur=
rimus violentia/vt illos cum gladijs mucronibuſꞇ̃
nr̃is cominus attigeremus. Quoſꝗdẽ cũ ꝑſenſiſſent
oẽs in fugã ꝑ ſiluas & nemora cõuerſi ſũt/ac nos cã
pi victores(interfectis ex eis vulneratiſꞇ̃ plurimis)
deſeruerũt.Hos aũt ꝓ die illa lõgiore fuga nequaꞇ̃
inſeꝗ voluimus/ob id ꝗ fatigati nimiũ tũc eſſemus
ꝗn potius ad naues nr̃as cũ tãta ſeptẽ illoꝝ qui no=
biſcũ venerãt remeauimus lęticia: vt tñ in ſe gaudi
um vix ipſi ſuſcipẽ poſſẽt. Seꝗnti autẽ aduẽtãte dr̃e
vidimus ꝑ inſulã ipſam:copiofam gentium appro=
pinquare cateruam/ cornibus inſtrumentiſꞇ̃ alijs
(quibus in bellis vtuntur)buccinantem/qui & quo

quę depicti omnes ac varijs volucrũ plumis ornati
erãt.Ita vt intueri mirabile foret/quibus pceptis ex
inito rurſum inter nos deliberauimus conſilio: vt ſi
gens hęc nobis inimicicias pararet/noſmet omnes
in vnũ cõgregaremus/videremuſcʒ mutuo ſemper
ac interim ſatageremus vt amicos nobis illos effice
remus/quibus amiciciã noſtrã nõ recipiẽtibus:illos
qnaſi hoſtes tractaremus/ac quotʠt ex eis cõprehẽ
dere valeremus/ſeruos nr̃os ac mancipia ppetua fa
ceremus/& tunc armatiores vt potuimus/circa pla
gam ipſam ĩ gyrũ nos collegimus.Illi vero(vt puto
p̃ machinarũ noſtrarũ ſtupore)nos in terrã tunc mi
nime ꝓhibuerunt exilire.Exiuimus igĩt in eos ĩ ter
rã quadrifariã diuiſi. lvij. viri ſinguli decurionẽ ſuũ
ſequẽtes/& cũ eis longum manuale geſſimus bellũ
Verũtamẽ poſt diuturnã pugnã/plurimumcʒ certa
mẽ/necnõ interemptos ex eis multos/omnes in fu
gã coegimus:& ad vſcʒ populationẽ eorum vnam
ꝓſecuti fuimus:vbi cõprehẽſis ex eis.xxv. captiuis
eandẽ eorum populationẽ igni cõbuſſimus/& inſu
per ad naues nr̃as cum ipſis.xxv.captiuis repedaui
mus/interfectis ex eadem gente/vulneratiſcʒ pluri
mis/ex nr̃is aũt interempto dũtaxat vno:ſed vulne
ratis.xxij.qui oẽs ex dei adiutorio ſanitatẽ recupe
rauerunt. Cęterũ aũt recurſu in patriã p nos delibe
rato ordinatocʒ viri ſeptẽ illi/ qui nobiſcũ illuc ve
nerãt:quoꝝ quincʒ in pręmiſſo bello vulnerati ex

titerãt phaſelo vno in inſula illa arrepto/cũ captiuis
ſeptẽ(quos illis tribuimus) tres videlicet viros/ &
quattuor mulieres in terrã ſuã cum gaudio magno/
magna viriũ noſtrarum admiratione regreſſi ſunt.
Noſᑉ hyſpaniẹ viã ſequentes/Caliciũ tandẽ repe‑
tiuimus portũ:cũ.CC.xxij.captiuatis perſonis.xv.
Octobris die. Anno dñi. M.cccc. xcix. Vbi lẹtiſſi‑
me ſuſcepti fuimus/ac vbi eoſdẽ captiuos nr̃os ven
didimus:Et hẹc ſunt quẹ in hac nauigatione noſtra
priore/notatu digniora conſpeximus.

'De ſecundariẹ nauigationis curſu.

Vantum ad ſecundariẹ nauigatiõis curſum
q   & ea quẹ in illa memoratu digna conſpexi/
dicet̃ in ſequẽtibus. Eandẽ igit̃ inchoantes
nauigationẽ Calicium exiuimus portum Anno dñi
M. cccc. lxxxix. xi. Maij die. Quo exitu factu nos
curſum noſtrũ Campiuiridis ad inſulas arripientes
necnõ ad inſularũ magnẹ Canariẹ viſum tranſabeũ
tes in tantũ nauigauimus vt inſulẹ cuidã q̃ ignis in‑
ſula dicit̃ applicaremus/vbi facta nobis de lignis &
aqua puiſione/& nauigatiõe nr̃a rurſum p̃ Lebec‑
cium ventũ incepta.Poſt enauigatos.xix.dies/ter‑
rã quandã nouà tandẽ tenuimus/ quã quidẽ firmã
exiſtere cenſuimus cõtra illam de qua facta in ſupe
rioribus mẽtio eſt/& q̃ quidẽ terra in zona torrida

d

extra lineã ęquinoctialem ad partē auftri fita eft:fu
pra quã meridionalis polus fe.v. exaltat gradibus/
extra qd'cunçp'clima/ diftatçp eadē terra a p̄noiatis
infulis(vt p Lebecciũ ventũ cõftabat) leucis. ccccc.
In q̃ terra dies cũ noctibus ęq̃les.xxvij. Iunij cũ fol
in cancri tropico eft/ exiftere reperimus. Eandē ter
rã in aquis oĩno fubmerfam/necnõ magnis flumini
bus pfufam effe inuenimus/q̃ & quidē femet pluri
mũ viridē: & ̦pceras altiffimafçp arbores habētem
mõftrabat:vñ neminē in illa effe tũc pcepimus. Tũ
vero cõftitimus/ & claffem noftrã anchorauimus:
folutis nõnullis phafelis/cũ qbus in terrã ipfam ac̸
cedere tentauimus. Porro nos aditũ in illã querētes
& circũ eã fepius gyrãtes:ipam vt p̄tactũ eft/fic flu
minũ vndis vbiçp pfufam iuenimus:vt nufçp locus
effet/q̃ maximis aquis nõ immadefceret. Vidimus
tñ interim p flumina ipfa/figna q̃ꝫmulta/ queadmo
dũ ipfa eadē tellus inhabitata effet/ & icolis multis
fecũda. At qm̃ eadē figna cõfideraturi: i ip̄am defcē
dere nequiebamus:ad naues ñras reuerti concorda
uimus:qd' & qdē fęcimus. Quibus ab hic exancho
ratis:poftea inter Leuantē & Seroccũ ventũ:colla̸
teraliꝭ fcd'm terrã(fic fpirãte vēto)nauigauimus/p̸
tentãtes fepius interim/p̄ribus q̃ꝫ.xl.durãtibus leu̸
cis/fi in ipfam penetrare infulã valeremus. Qui la̸
bor oĩs inanis extitit. Cum fiqdē illo in latere maris
fluxũ q̃ a Serocco ad magiftralē abibat fic violentũ

cõperimus:vt idẽ mare ſe nauigabile nõ p̃beret: q̃•
bus cognitis incõueniẽtibus/conſilio facto cõueni•
mus:vt nauigiũ nr̃m p mare ad magiſtralẽ reflecte•
remus. Tũcꝗ ſcd̃m terrã ipſam intm̃ nauigauimus:
vt tãdẽ portui vni applicaremus:q belliſſimã inſulã
belliſſimũcꝗ ſinũ quẽdã in eius ĩgreſſu tenebat/ſup̃
quẽ nobis nauigãtibus vt ĩ illũ introire poſſemus: ĩ
mẽſam in inſula ipſa gentiũ turbã a mari q̃ttuor leu
cis aut circic̃ diſtãtẽ vidimus. Cuius rei gr̃a lꝗtati nõ
parũ extitimus. Igic̃ paratis nauiculis nr̃is: vt ĩ eãdẽ
inſulã vaderemus:lintrẽ quãdã in q̃ pſone cõplures
erãt:ex alto mari venire vidimus: ꝓpter qd̃ tũc cõ•
uenimus vt eis iuaſis ipſos cõpr̃ĕderemus. Et tũc
illos nauigare & in gyrũ(ne euadere poſſent)circũ•
dare occepimus/q̃bus ſua quocꝗ vice nitẽtibus/vi•
dimus illos(aura tẽporata manẽte)remis ſuis oibus
ſurſum erectis/q̃ſi firmos ac reſiſtẽtes ſe ſignificare
velle: quã rẽ ſic idcirco illos efficere putauimus/ vt
inde nos ĩ admiratiõe cõuerterẽt. Cũ ꝟo ſibi nos
cominus appropinꝗre cognouiſſent: remis ſuis in
aquã cõuerſis:terrã ꝟſus remigare ĩcepert̃. At tunc
nobiſcũ carbaſũ vnã. xlv. doliorꝗ volatũ celerrimã
educebamus:q̃ tũc tali nauigio delata ẽ:vt ſb̃ito vẽ
tũ ſup eos obtineret. Cũcꝗ irruẽdi ĩ illos adueniſſet
cõmoditas:ipſi ſeſe appatũcꝗ ſuũ ĩ phaſelo ſuo ordi
nate ſpargẽtes/ ſe q̃cꝗ ad nauigãdũ accinxert̃. Itacꝗ
cũ eos p̃terijſſemus tunc fugere conati ſunt. At nos

d ij

nõnullis tunc expeditis phaſelis/validis virĩs ſtipa⸗
tis:illos tunc cõprehēdere putãtes mox in eos incur
rimus/cõtra q̃s bis geminis vere horis/nobis nitēti
bus/niſi carbaſus nr̃a q̃ curſu eos p̄terierat rurſum
ſup eos reuerſa fuiſſet/illos penitus amittebamus.
Cum v̊o ipſi ſe eiſdē noſtris phaſelis carbaſoc̢ vn⸗
dic̢ cõſtrictos eſſe pſpicerēt: oēs q̃ circit.xx.erant:
& a terra duabus fere leucis diſtabãt/in mari ſaltu
pſilierunt. Quos nos cũ phaſelis noſtris tota pſe⸗
quentes die/nullos ex eis (niſi tantũmodo duos)p̄⸗
hendere potuimus:alĳs oĩbus in terrã ſaluis abeũti
bus.In lintre autē eor̢ quã deſeruerant/bis gemini
iuuenes extabant/nõ de eor̢ gente geniti:ſed quos
in tellure aliena rapuerãt/ quor̢ ſingulis ex recenti
vulnere virilia abſciderãt/q̃ res admiratiõe nõ par
uam nobis attulit. Hos autē cum in nr̃as ſuſcepiſſe
mus nauiculas/nutibus nobis inſinuarũt:queadmo
dũ illi eos/ab ipſis manducãdos abducerũt/ indicã⸗
tes interim/qd̓ gens hęc tã effera & crudelis /huma
narũ carniũ comeſtrix Cambali nũcuparet̃. Poſtea
autē nos ipſam eor̢ lintrē nobiſcũ trahētes/& cum
nauiculis noſtris/curſum terrã eor̢ verſus arripien
tes/parũper interim conſtitimus: & naues nr̃as me
dia tantũ leuca a plaga illa diſtantes anchorauimus
quã in populũ plurimũ ob errare vidiſſemus:in illã
cum ipſis nauiculis nr̃is ſubito pperauimus/ductis
nobiſcũ duobus illis/ quos in lintre a nobis inuaſa

cõprehenderamus. Quã primũ autẽ terrã ipſam pe
de cõtigimus/omnes trepidi & ſeipſos abdituri in
vicinas nemorom latebras diffugerunt. Tum verõ
vno ex illis q̃s prc̨hẽderamus/abire p̃miſſio/& plu
rimis illi amiciciç̨.ſignis/necnon nolis/cymbalis/ac
ſpeculis pleriſq̧ datis/diximus ei ne p̨pter nos cętẽ
ri qui aufugerãt expaueſcerẽt/ qm̃ eorʒ amicos eſſe
plurimũ cupiebamus/qui abiens iuſſa noſtra ſolerẽ
impleuit/gente illa tota.cccc. videlicet fere viris/ cũ
feminis multis a ſiluis ſecũ ad nos eductis.Qui iner
mes ad nos vbi cũ nauiculis noſtris eramus omnes
venerũt/& cũ quibus tuuc amiciciã bonã firmaui₅
mus.reſtituto quoq̧ eis alio quem captiuũ teneba
mus/& pariter eorʒ lintrem quã inuaſeramus p̨ na₅
uiũ noſtrarũ ſocios/apud quos erat/ eis reſtitui mã
dauimus. Porro hęc eorʒ linter/quę ex ſolo arboris
trunco cauata:& multũ ſubtiliter effecta fuerat/lõ₅
ga.xxvi.paſſibus.& lata duobus brachijs erat.Hãc
cũ a nobis recuperaſſent & tuto in loco fluminis re
poſuiſſent omnes a nobis repente fugerũt/nec no₅
biſcũ amplius cõuerſari voluerũt.Quo tam barba
ro facto comperto/illos malę fidei maleq̧ conditio
nis exiſtere cognouimus. Apud eos aurũ dũtaxat
pauculum:quod ex auribus geſtabant vidimus. Ita
q̧ plaga illa relicta & ſecundũ eam nauigatis.lxxx.
circiter leucis ſtationẽ quãdam nauiculis tutam re₅
perimus: in quã introeuntes/ tãtas i.ibi cõperimus

gentes:vt id mirabile foret. Cum quibus facta amí
cicia iniuimus:deinde cum eis ad plures eorͣ pagos
vbi multum fecure/multūcͣ honefte ab eis fufcepti
fuimus/& ab eis interim.ccccc. vniones vnica nola
emimus:cum auro modico quod eis ex gratia cōtu
limus. In hac terra vinū ex fructibus fementibufcͣ
expreffum:vt ciceram ceruifiamve albam & ruben
tē bibunt:melius autē ex myrre pomis valde bonis
confectum erat/ex quibus cum multis cͣbonis alijs
fructibus guftui fapidis: & corpi falubribus habun
danter comedimus / propterea cͣ tempeftiue illuc
adueneramus. Hͨc eadem infula eorum rebus fup
pellectilive cͣmultum habundans eft/ genfcͣ ipfa
bone conuerfationis/& maioris pacificentiͤ eft/ cͣ
vfcͣ alibi reͣerimus aliã. In hoc portu. xvij.diebus
cum ingenti placito perftitimus / veniͤtibus quoti⸗
die ad nos populis multis/ nos effigiemcͣ noftram
& albedinem necnon veftimēta armacͣ noftra/ &
nauium noftrarum magnitudinē admirãtibus. Híj
etiam nobis gentem quandam eis infeftam/ occidē
tem verfus exiftere retulerunt/quͤ gens infinitã ha
bebant vnionum quantitatē/quot cͣ quos ipfi ha⸗
bebant vniones eifdem inimicis fuis in belligeratio
nibus aduerfus eos habitis abftulerant: nos quocͣ
& quͤadmodū illos pifcarenͭ/ & quͤadmodū na⸗
fcerenͭ edͦcentes/quorū dicta vera ͣfecto effe co
gnouimus:ͣput & maieftas veftra pofthͤc amplius

intelligere poterit. Relicto autē portu illó: & ſcďm
plagā eandē in quā cōtinue gentes affluere ͵pſpicie
bamus/curſu noſtro ͵pducto/ portū quendā aliū re
ficiende vniuꝫ nauiculę noſtrę gr̄a ſubiuimus/in ꝗ̃
gentē multā eſſe cōperimus/ cū quibus nec vi/ nec
amicicia cōuerſationē obtinere valuimus/ illis ſi qn̄
· ꝗ̃ꝫ ı̄ terrā cū nauiculis nr̄is deſcēderemus/ ſe cōtra
nos aſpere defendētibus/& ſi qn̄cꝫ nō ſuſtinere nō
valerēt in ſiluas aufugientibus: & nos nequaꝗ̃ex⸗
pectātibus:quorꝫ tantā barbariē nos cognoſcentes
ab eis exhinc diſceſſimus. Tunccꝫ inter nauigandū
inſulā quandā in mari leucis a terra.xv. diſtātē vidi
mus quā ſi in ea populus quiſpiā eſſet inuiſere con⸗
cordanimus.ln illā igit̄ accelerātes quandā inibi in⸗
uenimus gentē/quę oı̄m beſtialiſſima ſimpliciſſima
cꝫ/omniū quocꝫ gratioſiſſima benigniſſimacꝫ erat
cuiuſquidē gentis ritus & mores eiuſmodi ſunt.

De eiuſdem gentis ritu & moribus.

h   I vultu ac geſtu corporis brutales admo⸗
dum extant/ſingulicꝫ maxillas herba qua
viridi introrſum repletas habebāt/ quā pe
cudum inſtar vſcꝫ ruminabāt/ ita vt vix quiccꝫ elo
qui poſſent/ quorꝫ ꝗ̃cꝫ ſinguli ex collo puſillas ſicca
taſcꝫ cucurbitas duas/ alterā herba ipſa quam i ore
tenebant/ alterā vero ſarina quadam albida/ ę ipſo

minuto ſimili plenã/gerebant/habito bacillo quo
dam/quõ in ore ſuo madefactũ maſticatumcp ſepi/
us/in cucurbitam farrina repletã mittebant: & dein
de cum eo de eadem farrina extrahebant: quam ſibi
poſt hęc in ore vtrimcp ponebant herbã ipſam quã
in ore geſtabant eadẽ farrina reſpergitãdo/& hoc
frequentiſſime paulatimcp efficiebant: quam rẽ nos
admirati/illius cauſam ſecretũcp/aut cur ita facerẽt
ſatis nequiuimus cõprẽhẽdere. Heccine gens(vt ex
perimẽto didicimus)ad nos adeo familiariter aduę/
nit/ac ſi nobiſcũ ſepius antea negociati fuiſſent &
longęuam amiciciã habuiſſent. Nobis autẽ per pla
gam ipſam cum eis ambulantibus colloquẽtibuſcp
& interim recentẽ aquam bibere deſiderãtibus/ipſi
per ſigna/ſe talibus aquis penitus carere inſinuan/
tes/vltro de herba farinacp quam in ore geſtabant
offerebant/propter quod regionem eandem aquis
deficientem/cp cp vt ſitim ſubleuarent ſuam herbã
farinam talem in ore geſtarent intelleximus. Vnde
factum eſt: vt nobis ita meantibus/& circum pla/
gam eandem vna die cum media illos concomitan/
tibus/viuidam aquam nuſcp inuenerimus/cogno/
uerimuſcp cp ea quam bibebãt aqua ex rore/noctu
ſuper certis folijs: auriculis aſini ſimilibus decidẽte
collecta erat. Quęquidẽ folia eiuſmodi rore: no ctur
no tempore ſe implebant/ex quo rore qui optimus
eſt/idem populus bibebat: ſed tamen talibus folijs

pſera eorũtq̃ doʒa deficiebant. Haccine gens victualibus qũg in terra ſolida ſunt/penitus carent/quin
immo ex piſcibus q̃s in mari piſcantur viuũt. Etenĩ
apud eos (qui magni piſcatores exiſtunt) piſcium
ingens habũdat copia/ex quibus ipſi plurimos tur
tures ac q̃ bonos piſces alios plures vltro nobis ob
tulerũt. Eorum vxores herba quam in ore viri ipſi
gerebant/nuſq̃ vtebantur. Verum ſingulę cucurbitam vnam aqua impletam/ex qua biberent habe
bant. Nullos domorʒ pagos/nullave tuguria gens
hęc habent/preterq̃ folia grandia quędam/ſub qui
bus a ſolis feruore: ſed non ab ymbribus ſe prote-
gunt/propter quod autumabile eſt/q̃ parum in ter
ra illa pluitet. Cum autē ad piſcandum mare adie-
rint/folium vnũ adeo grande ſecum quiſq̃ piſcattu
rus effert/vt in illo in terram defixo/& ad ſolis mea
tum verſato/ſub illius vmbra aduerſus ęſtũ totum
ſe abſcondat. Haccine in inſula/q̃ multa variorʒ ge
nerum animalia ſunt/quę omnia aquam lutulētam
bibunt. Vidētes autē q̃ in ea comodi nihil naſciſce
remur/nos relicta illa/alia quandā inſulā tenuimus:
in quam nos ingredientes/& recentem vnde bibe-
remus aquā inueſtigantes/putantes interim ipſam
eandem terram a nullis eſſe habitatā/propterea q̃
in ea neminē inter adueuiendum ,pſpexeramus/dũ
per arena deambularemus/ veſtigia pedum q̃ magna nonnulla vidimus/ ex quibus cenſuimus q̃ ſi

d v

eiſdẽ pedibus reliqua membra reſpondebant/ ho‑
mines in eadem terra grandiſſimi habitabant. No‑
bis autẽ ita ꝑ arenam deambulantibus/viam vnam
in terrã ducentẽ comperimus/ ſecundum quam.ix.
de nobis euntes/inſulam ipſam inuiſere parauimus
ob id ꝙ non ꝗ̃ſpacioſam illam/ nec ꝗ̃ multas in ea
habitare gentes exiſtimauimus. Pererrata igitur ſe
cundum eandem viã: vna fere leuca/quinqꝫ in con‑
ualle quadam(quę populate apparebant) vidimus
caſas/in quas introeuntes quinqꝫ in illis reperimus
mulieres/vetulas videlicet duas & iuuenculas tres
que quidem omnes ſic ſtatura ꝓceres erãt/ vt inde
valde miraremur. Hę autẽ protinus vt nos intuitę
ſunt/adeo ſtupefactę ꝑmanſerũt: vt aufugiendi ani
mo penitus deficerẽt. Tumqꝫ vetulę ipſę lingua eo
rũ nobiſcũ blandiuſcule loquẽtes/ & ſeſe omnes in
caſam vnam recipiẽtes/ꝑ multa nobis de ſuis victu
alibus obtulerũt. Eedẽ vero omnes/ longiſſimo viro
ſtatura grandiores erant/& quidẽ ęque grãdes/ vt
Franciſcus de Albicio/ſed meliore ꝗ̃ nos ſumus ꝓ
portiõe compactę. Quibus ita compertis/ poſthęc
vna conuenimus: vt iuueuculis ipſis ꝑ vim arreptis
eas in Caſtiliã quaſi rem admirandã abduceremus/
in qua deliberatione nobis exiſtẽtibus/ecce.xxxvi.
vel circiter viri: multo ꝗ̃ fęmine ipſe altiores: & adeo
egregię cõpoſiti: vt illos inſpicere delectabile foret
caſam ipſam introire occeperũt/ ꝓpter quos tanta

tũc affecti fuimus animi turbatione: vt fatius apud
nauiculas nr̃as q̃ cũ tali gente eſſe duxiſſemus. Hĩj
etẽm ingentes arcus & ſagittas necnõ & ſudes p̃ti#
caſue magnas inſtar clauarũ ferebãt/ qui ingreſſi lo
quebantur quoq̃ inter ſe mutuo:ac ſi nos compre#
hendere vellẽt. Quo tali periculo percepto/ diuerſa
etiã inr̃ nos tũc fẽcimus cõſilia. Vnis vt illos in ipſa
eadẽ caſa inuaderemus: aliǰs ỹo nequaq̃:ſed foris
potius & ĩ platea:& aliǰs vt nuſq̃ aduerſus eos pu
gnam quereremus/donec q̃d agere vellẽt intellige#
remus aſſeuerantibus.Inter q̃ conſilia/caſam illã ſi#
mulate exiuimus: & ad naues nr̃as remeare occepi
mus:ipſiq̃(q̃tus eſt lapidis iactus)mutuo ſp loquẽ
tes nos inſecuti ſunt/haud minore q̃ nos(vt autu#
mo) repediãtes formidine/ cũ nobis manẽtibus ipſi
quoq̃ eminus manerent/ & niſi nobis ambulanti#
bus nõ ambularẽt.Cum ỹo ad naues noſtras perti
giſſemus:& in illas ex ordine ĩtroiremus/ mox oẽs
ĩn mare proſilierunt/ & q̃ multas poſt nos ſagittas
ſuas iaculati ſunt:ſed tũc eos p̃paucũ metuebamus
Nã tũ machinarꝛ nr̃aꝛ duas ĩ eos(potius vt terre#
rẽt q̃ vt interirẽt)emiſimus: quarũquidẽ tumultu
p̃cepto:oẽs cõfeſtim ĩ mõtẽ vnũ p̃piquũ ſuga abie
rũt:& ita ab eis erepti fuimus diſceſſimuſq̃ pir̃. Hĩj
oẽs nudi(vt de p̃oribꝰ hĩtũ eſt)eunt. Appellauimuſ
q̃ inſulã illã gigãtũ(ob p̃ceritatẽ eoꝛ)inſulã. Noꝝ
aũtvlr̃ius & a terra paulo diſtãtius trãſremigãtibus

ſepius interdum cum eis pugnaſſe nobis accidit: ob
id cp quicᵹ a tellure ſua ſibi tolli nequacᵹ permitte
re vellent. Et vticᵹ quidem repetundę Caſtilie pro⸳
poſitum iam nobis in mentem ſubierat / ob id potiſ
ſimum / cp vno iam fere anno in mari perſtiteramus
nec niſi tenuem alimentorũ neceſſariorũcᵹ aliorum
munitionẽ retinebamus. Quę, & quidẽ adhuc ex
vehementibus (quos pertuleramus) ſolis caloribus
iã cõtaminata inquinatacᵹ erãt / cũ ab exitu noſtro
a Campiuiridis inſulis vſcᵹ tunc / cõtinue per torri⸳
dam nauigauiſſemus zonam / & tranſuerſim per li⸳
neam ęquinoctialem bis: vt pręhabitum eſt. In qua
quidem voluntate nobis perſeuerantibus: nos a la⸳
boribus ſubleuare noſtris ſanctifico cõplacuit ſpiri
tui. Nempe receptũ quempiam pro rurſum nouã⸳
dis naualibus noſtris / nobis quęrentibus / ad gentẽ
quandam peruenimus / quæ nos cũ maxima ſuſce⸳
pit amicicia / & quaſquidem vnionũ perlarũve ori⸳
entalium comperimus in numero maximo tenere / ⸳
ppter quod. xlvij. diebus ibi perſtitimus &. C. xix.
vnionũ marchas / precio (vt eſtimabamus). xl. non
ſuperãte ducatos / ab eis cõparauimus. Nam nolas / ⸳
ſpecularia / criſtalinoſcᵹ nũnullos / necnon leuiſſima
electri ſolia quędam / eis tantũ ppterea tradidimus.
Nempe quotquot quilibet eorum obtineret vnio⸳
nes / eos p ſola nola donabat. Didicimus quocᵹ in⸳
terdum ab eis / quomodo & vbi illos piſcarentur.

qui & quidem oſtreolas/in quibus naſcunt̄/nobis
plures largiti ſunt. Et pariter nōnullas mercati fuiⸯ
mus:vbi in quibuſdam.C.&. xxx. vniones in quiⸯ
buſdam vero non totidem reperiebant̄. Noueritꝗ
maieſtas veſtra/ ꝗ niſi ꝑmaturi ſint & a conchiliȷs
in quibus gignuntur per ſeſe excidant/omninō per
fecti nō ſunt. Q uinimmo in breui)vt ſepius ipſe ex
pertus ſum(emarceſcūt: & in nihil redacti ſunt. Cū
vero maturi fuerint in oſtrea ipſa inter carnes(prēⸯ
ter id ꝗ ipſis carnibus hereāt)ſe ſeparāt/ & huiuſce
modi optimi ſunt. Effluxis igit̄. xlvȷȷ. diebus/ necnō
gente illa/quam nobis plurimū amicā effeceramus
relicta/ hinc ab eis exceſſimus ob plurimarū rerum
noſtrarū indigentiam/ venimuſꝗ ad Antiglię inſⷤ
lam quā paucis nuper ab annis Criſtophorus Coⸯ
lumbus diſcooperuit/in q̄ reculas noſtras ac nauaⸯ
lia reficiēdo/menſibus duobus & diebus totidē per
manſimus/plures interdum Chriſticolarū inibi cōⸯ
uerſantium cōtumelias perpetiendo quas prolixus
ne nimium fiam hic omitto. Eandem vero inſulam
xxȷȷ.Iulȷȷ deſerentes/percurſa vnius mēſis cum meⸯ
dio nauigatione Calicium tandem portum. vȷȷȷ.mē
ſis Septembris ſubiuimus/ vbi cum honore ꝑfectu
ꝗ ſuſcepti fuimus. Et ſic per dei placitum finem nō
ſtra cœpit ſecunda nauigatio.

De tertio facta nauigatione.

E in Sibillia exiftente/ & a pœnis atꝗ laboribus quos inter p̄memoratas pertule-
ram nauigationes paulifper requiefcente/
defiderateꝗ pofthęc in perlarum terram remeare
fortuna fatigationũ mearnm nequaꝗ adhuc fatura
fereniſſimo illi dño Manueli Portugalię regi mifit
in cor(nefcio vt quid) vt deftinato nuncio litteras
regales fuas ad me tranfmitteret quibus plurimum
rogabat vt ad eum apud Lifbonã celerius me tranf-
ferrem:ipfe etem̄ mirabilia mihi plurima faceret. Su
per qua re nondum tunc deliberaui:quinimmo ei p
eundẽmet nuncium/ me minus bene difpofitum &
tunc male habere fignificaui. Verũ ſi quandoꝗ re-
conualefcerẽ & maieftati eius regię meũ forfan cõ-
placeret obfequium/omnia quęcunꝗ vellet ex ani
mo perficerẽ. Qui rex percipiẽs ꝗ me ad fe tũc tra-
ducere nequiret Iulianũ Bartholomeũ Iocundũ qui
tunc in Lifbona erat rurfum ad me deftinauit cum
cõmiſſione vt oibus modis me ad eundẽ regẽ fecũ
perduceret: ꝓpter cuius Iuliani aduentũ & preces
coactus tũc fui ad regẽ ipfum meare/ quod(qui me
nouerant omnes)malũ eſſe iudicarunt. Et ita a Ca-
ftilia vbi honor mihi non m̄odicus exhibitus extite
rat/ac rex ipfe Caftilie exiftimationẽ de me bonam
cõceperat profectus fum:& qd' deterius fuit/hofpi
te infalutato/ ac mox coram ipfo rege domino Ma
nuele meipfum obtuli; qui rex de aduentu meo nõ

paruam vifus eft cõcepiffe leticiam/plurimum me
interdum rogitans/ v t vna cum tribus eius confer∽
uantiȩ nauibus/quȩ ad exeundum & ad nouarum
terrarum inquifitionem prȩparatȩ erant proficifci
vellem. Et ita(quia regum preces præcepta funt)ad
eius votum confenfi.

Tempus profectionis tertiȩ

Gitur ab hoc Lifbonȩ portu cũ tribus cõ∽
feruantiæ nauibus die Maij decima. M;
ccccc. & primo/abeuntes/curfum noftrũ
verfus magnȩ Canariȩ infulas arripuimus : fecun∽
dũ quas & ad earum profpectum inftanter enaui∽
gantes idem nauigium noftrũ collateraliter fecun∽
dum Affricam occidentẽ verfus fecuti fuimus. Vbi
pifciũ quorundam(quos Parghi nuncupant)mul∽
titudinem maximam in ȩquore prȩdidimus/tribus
inibi diebus morã facientes. Exinde autem ad par∽
tem illam Ethopiȩ / quæ Befilicca dicitur deueni∽
mus / quæ quidem fub torrida zona pofita eft/ &
fuper quã quattuordecim gradibus fe Septentrio∽
nalis erigit polus in climate primo vbi diebus vn∽
decim nobis de lignis & aqua prouifionem paran∽
tes reftitimus / propter id cɋ Auftrum verfus per
Athlanticum pelagus/ nauigandi mihi ineffet affe∽
ctus. Itacɋ portũ Ethiopiȩ illũ poft hȩc relinquẽtes

nunc per Lebeccium ventū in tātum nanigauimus
vt.lx.&.vij.infra dies infulę cuidam applicuerimus
quę infula.DCC.a portu eodem leucis ad Lebeccij
partē diſtaret. In quibuſquidē diebus/peius perpeſ
ſi tempus fuimus q̃ vnq̃ in mari quiſq̃ antea ptu⸗
lerit/ppter ventor nimborūue impetus/qui q̃plu
rima nobis intulere grauamina ex eo q̃ nauigiū no
ſtrum lineę pręſertim equinoctiali continue iunctū
fuit.Inibicq̃ in menſe Iunio hyems extat ac dies no⸗
ctibus ęquales ſunt/atq̃ ipſę vmbrę noſtrę cōtinue
verſus meridiem erant. Tandem vero omnitonan⸗
ti placuit nouam vnam nobis oſtendere plagā.xvij
ſcilicet Auguſti/iuxta quā(leuca ſepoſiti ab eadem
cum media)reſtitimus/& poſtea aſſumptis cymbis
nōnullis in ipſam viſuri ſi inhabitata eſſet/ profecti
fuimus:quā & quidē incolas plurimos habitare re⸗
perimus qui beſtijs prauiores erant/quemadmodū
maieſtas regia veſtra poſthęc intelliget. In hoc ỹo
introitus noſtri principio/gentem non percepimus
aliquā/q̃uis oram ipſam per ſigna plurima(quę vi
dimus) populo multo repletā eſſe intellexerimus.
De qua quidē ora pro ipſo ſereniſſimo Caſtilię re⸗
ge poſſeſſoriū cępimus/ inuenimuſcq̃ illam multū
amenam/ac viridem eſſe & appatętię bonę.Eſt au
tem extra lineā ęquinoctialem Auſtrum verſus.v.
gradibus/& ita eadem die ad naues noſtras repeda
uimus. Quia vero lignorum & aquę penuriam pa

ñebamur/cõcordauimus iterum in terrã/ altera die
reuerti/vt nobis de neceſſarijs ꝓuideremus: in qua
quidem nobis extantibus/ vidimus ſtãtes in vnius
montis cacumine gentes/ quę deorſum deſcendere
non auderent/ erantꝗ nudi omnes/ necnon conſi-
milis effigiei coloriſcꝗ/ vt de ſuꝓioribus habitũ eſt.
Nobis autẽ ſatagentibus vt nobiſcũ conuerſatũ ac
cederent/nõ ſic ſecuros eos efficere valuimus vt de
nobis adhuc nõ diffiderent. Quorꝝ obſtinatione ꝓ
teruiacꝗ cognita/ ad naues ſub noctẽ remeauimus
relictis in terra(videntibus illis) nolis ſpeculiſcꝗ nõ
nullis ac rebus alijs. Cumcꝗ nos in mari eminus eſſe
proſpicerẽt/omnes de ipſo mõte(ꝓpter reculas ꝗs
reliqueramus)deſcenderunt/plurima inter ſe admi-
rationis ſigna facientes. Nec tunc de aliquo niſi de
aqua nobis ꝓuidimus. Craſtino autẽ effecto mane
vidimus e nauibus gentem eandem numero ꝗ antea maiorẽ/paſſim per terram ignes ſumoſcꝗ facien
tẽ. Vnde nos exiſtimantes/ cꝗ nos per hoc ad ſe in-
uitarent/iuimus ad eos in terram/vbi tũc populum
plurimum aduenisſe cõſpeximus: qui tamẽ a nobis
longe ſeipſos tenebant/ſigna facientes interim non
nulla: vt cum eis interius in inſulã vaderemus. Propter quod factũ eſt/ vt ex Chriſticolis noſtris duo
protinus ad hoc parati/ periculo ad tales eundi ſe-
metipſos exponerent: vt quales gentes ipſi forent:
aut ſi quas diuitias ſpecieſue aromaticas vllas habe

c

rent/ipfi cognofcerent: quapropter in tantū nauiū
prȩtorem rogitauerunt/vt eis quod poftulabāt an
nueret. Tum vero illi ad hoc fefe accingētes necnō
plerafcȝ de rebus fuis minutis/fecū fumentes/ vt in
de a gentibus eifdem/mercarent̃ alias: abierūt a no⸗
bis/data conditione: vt ad nos poft quincȝ dies ad
fummū remeare folliciti effent: nos etenim illos tam
diu expectaremus. Et ita tunc iter fuū in terrā arri⸗
puerunt/atcȝ nos ad naues noftras regreffum cȩpi
mus vbi expectando eos diebus. viij. perftitimus.
In quibus diebus gens per multa noua dietim fere
ad plagam ipfam adueniebat/ fed nufcȝ nobifcum
colloqui voluerūt. Septima igit̃ aduentāte die nos
in terram ipfam iterū tendentes/gentē illam mulie⸗
res fuas omnes fecū adduxiffe reperimus. Quā ẙo
primū illuc peruenimus/ mox ex eifdem vxoribus
fuis ad colloquendū nobifcū cȝplures miferunt/ fȩ⸗
minis tamen eifdem/ non fatis de nobis·confidenti
bus: quod quidem nos attendentes cōcordauimus
vt iuuenem vnum e nobis(qui validis agilifcȝ nimi
um effet)ad eas quocȝ tranfmitteremus/& tunc vt
minus fȩmine eȩdē metuerent/in nauiculas noftras
introiuimus. Quo egreffio iuuene cum feipfum in⸗
ter illas immifcuiffet/ac ille omnes circūftantes con
tingerent palparentcȝ eum/& propter eum nō pa⸗
rū admirarentur: ecce interea de monte fȩmina vna
vallum magnum manu geftās aduenit/quȩ poftcȝ

vbi iuuenis ipſe erat appropiauit/ tali eum valli ſui
ictu a tergo percuſſit vt ſubito mortuus in terrã ex
cideret: quem confeſtim mulieres aliẹ corripiẽtes/ il
lum in montẽ a pedibus p̃traxerunt/ viricҩ ipſi qui
in monte erãt/ ad littus cũ arcubus & ſagittis adue
niẽtes/ ac ſagittas ſuas in nos coniicieutes/ tali gẽtẽ
noſtrã affecerũt ſtupore(ob id cҩ nauiculẹ illẹ ĩ qui
bus erat harenã nauigando radebãt/ nec celeriſ̃ au؛
fugere tunc poterant) vt ſumendorꝝ armorum ſuo؛
rum memoriam nemo tunc haberet. Et ita cҩplures
contra nos ſagittas ſuas eiaculabantur. Tum vero
in eos/ quattuor machinarũ noſtrarum fulmina(li؛
cet neminem attingentia) emiſimus/ quo audito to
nitruo/ omnes curſum in montẽ fugerunt/ vbi mu؛
lieres ipſẹ erãt/ quẹ iuuenẽ noſtrum quem trucida؛
uerant(nobis videntibus) in fruſtra ſecabãt/ necnõ
fruſtra ipſa nobis oſtentantes/ ad ingentem quem
ſuccenderant ignem torrebant/ & deinde poſthẹc
manducabant. Viri quocҩ ipſi ſigna nobis ſimiliter
facientes/ geminos Chriſticolas noſtros alios/ ſe pa
riformiter peremiſſe manducaſſecҩ inſinuabãt: qui
bus/ qui & vticҩ vera loquebantur/ in hoc ipſo cre
didimus. Cuius nos improperij vehemẽtius piguit:
cum immanitatem quam in mortuum exercebant:
oculis intueremur ipſi proprijs. Quamobrem plu؛
res quam quadraginta de nobis in animo ſtabili؛
ueramus / vt omnes pariter terram ipſam impetu

e ij

petentes tam immane factum tamcʒ beftialem fero
ciã vindicatũ vaderemus. Sed hoc ipfum nobis na⸱
uiprꝗor nõ permifit/& ita tam mãgnã ac tam gra⸱
uem iniuriã paffi/cũ maliuolo animo & grandi op⸱
probrio noftro(efficiẽte hoc naupreceptore nõ)
impunitis illis abfceffimus. Poftcʒ autẽ terrã illam
reliquimus/mox inter Leuantẽ & Seroccũ vẽtum
(fcd'm quos fe continet terra)nauigare occepimus:
plurimos ambitus/plurimofcʒ gyros/interdũ fectã
tes/ quibus durantibus/ gentes non vidimus/ quæ
nobifcum practicare aut ad nos appropinquare vo
luerint. In tantũ vero nauigauimus vt tellurem vnã
nouã(que fcd'm Lebeccium fe porrigeret) inueneri
mus. In qua cum campũ vnũ circuiuiffemus(cui fan
cti Vincentij campo nomen indidimus(fecundum
Lebeccium ventum pofthæc nauigare occepimus.
Diftatcʒ idẽ fancti Vincentij campus a priore ter⸱
ra illa vbi Chrifticolę nñi extiterunt interempti. cl.
leucis ad partẽ Leuãtis. Qui & quidẽ campus.viij.
gradibus extra lineã ꝗquinoctialem/ verfus auftrũ
eft. Cum igitur ita vagantes iremus/quadã die co⸱
piofam gentium multitudinem/nos nauiumcʒ no⸱
ftrarum vaftitatẽ mirantiũ/ in terra vna alia effe cõ
fpeximus/ apud quos tuto in loco mox reftitimus:
& deinde in terrã ipfam ad eos ex nauiculis noftri s
defcendimus/quos quidem mitioris effe conditio⸱
nis cʒ priores reperimus. Nam &fi in edomandis

illis diu elaborauimus/amicos tamē noſtros eos tā
dem effecimus: cum quibus negociando practican
do cꝗ varie.v.maſimus diebus vbi cānas fiſtulas vi
rides plurimū groſſas/& etiam nōnullas in arborū
cacuminibus ſiccas inuenimus.Cōcordauimus au⸗
tem vt ex eadem gēte duos/qui nos eorum linguā
edocerent/ inde traduceremus. Quamobrem tres
ex eis:vt in Portugalliam venirent/nos vltro comi
tati ſunt.Et qm̄ me omnia ꝑſequi ac deſcribere pi⸗
get/ dignetur veſtra noſſe maieſtas:cꝗ nos portum
illum linquentes/per Lebeccium ventum/ & in vi⸗
ſu terrę ſemper tranſcurrimus/plures continue faci
endo ſcalas plureſcꝗ ambitus/ ac interdum cū mul⸗
tis populis loquendo:donec tandē verſus auſtrum
extra Capricorni tropicū fuimus.Vbi ſuꝑ horizon
ta illū meridionalis polus.xxxíj. ſeſe extollebat gra
dibus/atcꝗ minorem iam perdideramus vrſam:ipſa
cꝗ maior vrſa multū infima videbāt/ſere in fine Ho
rizontis ſe oſtentans:& tūc per ſtellas alterius me⸗
ridionalis poli noſmetipſos dirigebamus/quę mul⸗
to plures/ multo cꝗ maiores ac lucidiores/ c̄ꝗ noſtri
poli ſtellę exiſtūt/propter qd'plurimarū illarū figu
ras confinxi/& prꝛeſertim earū quę prioris ac maio⸗
ris magnitudinis erant/vna cū declinatione diame⸗
trorū quas circa polum Auſtri efficiūt/ & vna cum
denotatione earundem diametrorū & ſemidiame⸗
trorū earū prout in meis quattuor dietis ſiue naui⸗

gationibus inſpici facile poterit. Hoccine ꝟo nauiᵉ
gio noſtro a campo ſancti Auguſtini incepto.Dcc.
percurrimus leucas videlicet ꝩſus Ponentem. c. &
verſus Lebecciũ. Dc. quaſquidē dum pagraremus
ſi quis quę vidimus enumerare vellet non totidem
ei papirę cartę ſufficerent. Nec quidem interdum
magni cõmodi res inuenimus demptis infinitis caᵉ
ſię arboribus:et pariter plurimis quę laminas certas
producunt/ cum quibus & miranda alia per multa
vidimus q̃ faſtidioſa recenſitu forent. Et in hac qui
dem peragratione.x.fere mēſibus extitimus.In qua
cognito ꝗ mineralia nulla reperiebamus/ conueni
mus vna vt abinde ſurgentes alio ꝑ mare euagareᵉ
mur. Quo inito inter nos conſilio/ mox edictũ fuit
ac in omnē cętum noſtrũ vulgatũ vt quicquid·in ta
li nauigatione pręcipiendum cenſerem/idipſum inᵉ
tegriter fieret. Propter quod cõfeſtim edixi manda
uicꝝ vbicꝝ/vt de lignis & aqua ꝑ ſex menſibus mu
nitionē omnes ſibi pararent(Nam per nauium maᵉ
giſtros nos cũ nauibus noſtris adhuc tantũdem na
uⁱgare poſſe indicatum eſt)qua quidem(quã edixe
ram)facta prouiſione/ nos oram illam linquētes &
inde nauigationē noſtrã per Seroccũ ventũ initian
tes Februarij.xiij. videlicet/cum ſol ęquinoctio iam
appropinquaret & ad hoc Septentrionis hemiſpeᵉ
rium noſtrũ vergeret in tantũ peruagati fuimus: vt
meridianũ polũ ſuper horizonta illum.lij.gradibus

ſublimatu inuenerimus. Ita vt nec minoris vrſę nec maioris/ſtellę ammodo inſpici valerēt. Nam tunc a portu illo a quo per Seroccum abieramus. ccccc. leucis longe iam facti eramus. iij. videlicet Aprilis. Qua die tempeſtas ac ꝓcella in mari tam vehemēs exorta eſt/ vt vela noſtra omnia colligere & cum ſolo nudoꝗ malo remigare compelleremur ꝓſtanſ te vehementiſſime Lebeccio ac mari intumeſcente & aere turbulentiſſimo extante. Propter quem tur binis violentiſſimū impetum noſtrates omnes non modico affecti fuerunt ſtupore. Noctes quoꝗ tūc inibi ꝗmaxime erant. Etenim Aprilis. vij. ſole cirſ ca arietis finem extāte ipſę eędem noctes horarum xv. eſſe repertę ſunt: hyemſꝗ etiam tunc inibi erat vt veſtra ſatis perpendere poteſt maieſtas. Nobis autem ſub hac nauigantibus turbulentia: terrā vnā Aprilis. ij. vidimus/ penes quam. xx. circiter leucas nauigantes appropiauimus. Verum illam omnimo do brutalem & extraneā eſſe comperimus/ in qua quidem nec portum quempiam/ nec gētes aliquas fore conſpeximus: ob id (vt arbitror) ꝗ tam aſpeſ rum in ea frigus algeret vt tam acerbum vix quiſ ꝗ perpeti poſſet. Porro in tanto periculo/ in tanſ taꝗ tempeſtatis importunitate noſmet tum reperi mus/ vt vix alteri alteros prę grandi turbine nos vi deremus. Quamobrem demum cum nauium pręſ tore pariter concordauimus vt connauitis noſtris

omnibus/terrã illam linquendi/seqȝ ab ea elongan̄
di/ & in Portugalliam remeandi ſigna faceremus.
Quod conſiliũ ſanum quidē & vtile fuit/ cũ ſi inibi
noĉte ſolũ adhuc illa pſtitiſſemus/diſperditi omnes
eramus.Nempe cũ hinc abȷ̄ſſemus tam grãdis die
ſequenti tempeſtas in mari excitata eſt/ vt penitus
obrui/perdite metueremus.Propter quod plurima
peregrinationũ vota/ necnõ alias c̄ȝplures cerimo
nias(prout nautis mos eſſe ſolet)tunc fȩcimus.Sub
quo tempeſtatis infortunio.v.nauigauimus diebus
demiſſis omnino velis.In qnibuſquidem.v. diebus
ec.&.l. in mari penetrauimus leucas/linȩ interdũ
ȩquinoĉtiali necnon mari & aurȩ temperatiori ſem
per appropinquando/per quod nos a prȩmiſſis eri
pere periculis altiſſimo deo placuit.Eratcȝ huiuſce
modi noſtra nauigatio ad tranſmontanũ ventũ &
grȩcũ/ob id cꝗ ad Ethiopiȩ latus pertingere cupie
bamus:a quo p maris Athlantici fauces eundo. M.
ccc.diſtabamus leucis. Ad illam autē p ſummitonã
tis gratià Maȷ bis quina pertigimus die.Vbi in pla
ga vna ad latus Auſtri(quȩ Serraliona dicitur).xv.
diebus noſipſos refrigerando fuimus. Et poſt hæc
curſum noſtrum verſus inſulas/Lyazori diĉtas/ar
ripuimus/ quȩquidem inſulȩ a Serraliona ipſa.Dcc.
&.l.leucis diſtabant:ad quas ſub Iulȷ finem perue
nimus/ & pariter. xv. inibi nos reſiciēdo pſtitimus
diebus . Poſt quos inde exiuimus/ & ad Liſbonȩ

noſtrę recurſum nos accinximus:a qua ad occiden∢
tis partē.ccc.ſepoſiti leucis eramus: & cuius tādem
deinde portū.M.D.ij. cum proſpera ſaluatione ex
eunctipotentis nutu rurſum ſubiuimus/cū duabus
dūtaxat nauibus:ob id ꝗ tertiā in Serraliona (ꝗ̄n
amplius nauigare nō poſſet)igni cōbuſſeramus. In
hac autē noſtra tertio curſa nauigatiōe.xvi. circiter
menſes ꝑmanſimus.e quibus. xi. abſꜩ tranſmonta
neꝫ ſtellę necnō & maioris vrſę minoriſue aſpectu
nauigauimus /quo tempore noſmetipſos per aliam
meridionalis poli ſtellā regebamus.Quę ſupius cō
memorata ſunt/quę in eadē noſtra tertio facta naui
gatione/relatu magis digna conſpexi.

De quartę nauigationis curſu.

Eliquum autē eſt: vt quę in tertia nauiga∢
tione noſtra ꝓſpexerim ediſſeram. Quia
vero iam pręlonga narratione ſatiſco/ &
quoꜩ hęc eadem nr̄a nauigatio ad ſperatū a nobis
finē minime ꝓducta eſt/ ob aduerſitatem infortuni
umve quoddā quod in maris Athlantici nobis acci
dit ſinu:idcirco breuior fiam.Igĩ ex Liſbonę portu
cum ſex cōſeruantię nauibus exiuimus cū ꝓpoſito
inſulam vnā verſus horizontē poſitā inuiſendi:quę
Melcha dicĩ & diuitiarum multarū famoſa/necnō
nauiū oīm ſiue a Gangetico ſiue ab Indico mari ve∢

f

nientium receptus ſiue ſtatio eſt/ quemadmodum
Calicia receptus ſiue hoſpitale oīm nauigantiū eſt/
qui ab oriente in occidentē & econuerſo vagantur
prout de hoc ipſo per Calicutię viā fama eſt. Quæ
quidem inſula Melcha plus ad occidentē Calicutia
vero ipſa plus ad meridiē reſpicit: quod idcirco co
gnouimus/quia ipſa in aſpectu.xxxiij. graduū poli
antarctici ſita eſt. Decima ergo Maij die. M.D.iij.
nobis vnde ſupra egredientibus/ curſum noſtrū ad
inſulas virides nuncupatas/ primo dixerimus. Vbi
rerum neceſſariū munimina/ necnō & plura diuer╱
ſorum modoꝝ refrigeramina ſumentes: &.xij. in╱
terdum inibi diebus ceſſantes:per ventum Seroccū
poſt hęc euanigare occepimus:cū nauidominus no
ſter tancꝗ preſumptuoſus capitoſuſcꝗ preter neceſ╱
ſitatem & omniū noſtrum vnanimitatem(ſed ſolū
vt ſeſe noſtri & ſex nauiū prepoſitū oſtentaret) iuſ
ſit vt in Serralionā Auſtralem Ethiopię terram ten
deremus. Ad quā nobis acceleratibus:& illam tan╱
dem in cōſpectu habentibus/ tam immanis & acer
ba ſuborta tempeſtas eſt/ ac ventus contrarius/ &
fortuna aduerſa inualuit:vt in ipſam(quam noſtris
ipſi videbamus oculis) per quatriduum applicare
non valuerimus: quinimmo coacti fuerimus vt illa
relicta ad priorem nauigationē noſtram regredere
mur.Quāquidē nos per Sudueſium(qui ventū eſt
inter meridiem & Lebecciū)reaſſumentes. ccc. per

illam artitudinem nauigauimus leucas. Vnde factũ
eſt vt nobis extra lineam ęquinoctialem tribus pe
ne gradibus iam tunc exiſtentibus/terra quędã(a q̃
xij.diſtabamus leucis)apparuerit:quę apparitio nõ
parua nos affecit admiratione. Terra etẽ illa/inſu
la in medio mari multũ alta & admirabilis erat/quę
leucis duabus longior & vna dilatatior non exiſte
bat: in qua quidem terra nuncꝗ quiſcꝗ hominũ aut
fuerat aut habitauerat: & nihilominus nobis inſoeli
ciſſima fuit.In illa eĩ p ſtolidum conſiliũ ſuũ & re
gimen/prefectus nauium noſter nauẽ ſuã perdidit.
Nempe illa a ſcopulo quodam eliſa/ & inde ꝓpter
hoc in rimas diuiſa/ſancti Laurentij nocte(quę Au
guſti.x. eſt)in mari penitus ſubmerſa extitit/ nihil
inde ſaluo manente/ demptis tantummodo nautis.
Eratcꝗ nauis eadem doliorum.ccc. in qua noſtre to
tius turbę totalis potentia erat. Cum autẽ omnes
circa illam ſatageremus:vt ſi forte ipſam a periculo
ſubtrahere valeremus:dedit mihi in mandatis idem
nauium prefectus:vt cũ nauicula vna receptũ quẽ
piam bonum vbi pupes noſtras ſecure omnes reci
pere poſſemus apud inſulam eandem inuentũ per
gere/ nolens tamen ipſe idem prefectus: vt nauem
meã(quę nouẽ nautis meis ſtipata: & ĩ nauis pericli
tantis adiutorio intenta foret) mecum tunc tradu
cerem:ſed ſolum vt edixerat portũ vnum inquiſitũ
irem/ & in illo nauem meã ipſam mihi reſtitueret.

f ij

QVARTA

Qua iuſſione recepta/ego vt mandauerat(ſumpta
mecū nautarū meoꝝ medietate)in inſulā ipſam(a q̄
iiij.diſtabamus leucis) properãs/pulcherrimū inibi
portū:vbi claſſem noſtram oēm tute ſatis ſuſcipere
poſſemus inueni.Quo cōperto.viij.ibidem diebus
eundē nauiū pꝛefectū cū reliqua turba expectando
pſtiti.Qui cū nō aduenirēt/moleſte nō parū ptuli
atꝗ qui mecū erãt ſic obſtupeſcebãt vt nullo cōſo⸝
lari modo vellent.Nobis autē in hac exiſtētibus an
guſtia/ipſa octaua die pupim vnã p ꝗquor aduēta⸝
re cōſpeximus/cui vt nos ꝑcipere poſſent mox ob
uiam iuimus cōfidentes ſperanteſꝗ vna qd'ad me
liorē portū quēpiam nos ſecū ducerēt.Quibus dū
nos appropinquaſſemus/& viciſſim nos reſalutaſ⸝
ſemus:retulerūt illi nobis/eiuſdē pꝛefecti noſtri na⸝
uē in mari penitus(demptis nautis)perditã extitiſſe
quꝫ nuncia(vt cōtēplari veſtra pōt regia maieſtas)
me nō parua affecerūt moleſtia/cum a Liſbona(ad
quã reuerti habebã).M.longe exiſtēs leucis/in lon
go remotoꝗ mari/me eſſe ſentirem.Nihilominus
tamen fortunꝫ noſmet ſubijcientes vlterius ꝓceſſi⸝
mus/reuerſiꝗ in primis fuimus ad memoratã inſu⸝
lã vbi nobis de lignis & aꝗ in conſeruatiꝫ meꝫ naui
ꝓuidimus.Erat ⱳo eadē inſula penitus inhoſpitata
inhabitataꝗ/multa aqua viuida & ſuaui in illa ſca⸝
turiente/cū infinitis arboribus innumeriſꝗ volucri
bus marinis & terreſtribus:quꝫ adeo ſimplices erãt

vt fefe manu comprehendi intrepide permitterent?
Propter quod tot tunc prendidimus vt nauiculam
vnã ex illis adimpleuerimus.In ea autē nulla alia in¬
uenimus animalia/ptercȝ mures cȝmaximos:& la¬
certas bifurcam caudam habentes cum nõnullis fer
pentibus quos etiã in ea vidimus.Igiť parata nobis
inibi ͵puifione fub vento inter meridiem & Lebec¬
ciũ ducente perreximus/ob id cȝ a rege mandatum
acceperamus:vt qualicũcȝ nõ obftante periculo/p̃
cedentis nauigationis viam infequeremur. Incepto
ergo huiufcemodi nauigio/ portũ tandē vnũ inue¬
nimus quē oĩm fanctoȝ Abbaciam nũcupauimus:
ad quē(͵pfperam annuente nobis aurã altiffimo) in
fra.xvij.pertigimus dies. Diftatcȝ idē portus.ccc. a
p̃fata infula leucis/in quoquidē portu nec p̃fectum
noftrũ/nec quemcȝ de turba alium reperimus/& fi
tamē in illo menfibus duobus & diebus quattuor
expectauerimus/quibus efluxis: vifo cȝ illuc nemo
veniret cõferuantia noftra tunc & ego concordaui
mus/vt fcd'm latus longius ͵pgrederemur. Percur¬
fis itacȝ. cc. lx. leucis portui cuidã alij applicuimus
in quo caftellũ vnũ erigere ͵ppofuimus/qd' & qui¬
dē ͵pfecto fecimus relictis in illo.xxiiij. Chrifticolis
nobifcũ exiftentibus/qui ex prȩfecti noftri pupe p̃
dita collecti fuerant.Porro in eodē portu prȩfatum
conftruendo caftellũ & brefilico pupes nr̃as onu¬
ftas efficiēdo.v. perftitimus menfibus/ ob id cȝ prȩ

nautaru perpaucitate & plurimoꝛ apparatuum ne
ceſſitate/longius ꝓgredi non valebamus. Quibus
ſuperioribus ita peractis/concordauimus poſt hęc
in Portugalliã reuerti/quã rem per gręcũ tranſmõ⸗
tanũ que ventum neceſſe nobis erat efficere. Relictis
igitur in caſtello prefato Chriſticolis.xxiiij. & cum
illis.xij. machinis ac alijs pluribus armis/vna cũ ꝓ⸗
uiſione ꝓ ſex menſibus ſufficiẽte/necnõ pacata no
biſcũ telluris illius gentec de qua hic minima ſit mẽ⸗
tio)licet infinitos inibi tunc viderimus/ & cum illis
practicauerimus. Nam.xl.fere leucas cũ.xxx. ex eis
in inſulam ipſam penetrauimus. Vbi interdum plu
rima pſpeximus. q̃ nũc ſubticeſcẽs libello meo. iiij.
nauigationum reſeruo. Eſt que eadẽ terra extra lineã
ęquinoctialẽ ad partẽ Auſtri.xviij.gradibus & ex⸗
tra Liſbonę meridianũ ad occidẽtis partem.xxxv.
ꝓput inſtrumenta noſtra monſtrabant/nos nauiga⸗
tionem noſtrã per Nornordenſium(qui inter grę⸗
cum tranſmontanũ que ventus eſt)cum animi ꝓpoſi
to ad hanc Liſbonę ciuitatẽ ꝓficiſcẽdi iniciantes/tã
dem poſt multos labores multa que pericula in hunc
eiuſdẽ Liſbonę portũ infra.lxxvij.dies.xxviij. Iunij
M.D.iiij.cum dei laude introiuimus. Vbi honorifi⸗
ce multũ & vltra que ſit credibile feſtiuę ſuſcepti fui⸗
mus:ob id ꝗ ipſa tota ciuitas nos in mari diſperdi⸗
tos eſſe exiſtimabat/quẽadmodũ reliqui omnes de
turba noſtra/ ꝑ ꝓfecti nr̃i nauiũ ſtultã ꝓſumptionẽ

extiterant. Quo superbiã modo iustus omniũ cen-
sor deus cõpensat. Et ita nunc apud Lisbonã ipsam
subsisto/ignorãs qd de me serenissimus ipse rex de
inceps efficere cogitet/ qui a tantis laboribus meis
iam exnunc requiescere plurimũ peroptarem/hunc
nunciũ maiestati vestrẹ plurimũ quoç interdũ cõ-
mendans.   Americus Vesputius in Lisbona.

Pressit/& ipsa eadẽ Christo monimẽta fauẽte
Tempore venturo cætera multa premet.

Vrbs Deodate tuo clarescens nomine præsul
Qua Vogesi montis sunt iuga pressit opus

Finitũ. iiij. kł. Septẽ
bris Anno supra ses
quimillesimũ. vij.

INTRODUCTION TO COSMOGRAPHY

WITH CERTAIN NECESSARY PRINCIPLES OF GEOMETRY AND ASTRONOMY

TO WHICH ARE ADDED

THE FOUR VOYAGES OF AMERIGO VESPUCCI

A REPRESENTATION OF THE ENTIRE WORLD, BOTH IN THE SOLID AND PROJECTED ON THE PLANE, INCLUDING ALSO LANDS WHICH WERE UNKNOWN TO PTOLEMY, AND HAVE BEEN RECENTLY DISCOVERED

DISTICH

Since God rules the stars and Cæsar the earth,
Nor earth nor stars have aught greater than these.

TO MAXIMILIAN CÆSAR AUGUSTUS

PHILESIUS, NATIVE OF THE VOSGES

Since thy Majesty is sacred throughout the vast world,
Maximilian Cæsar, in the farthest lands,
Where the sun raises its golden head from the eastern
    waves
And seeks the straits known by Hercules' name,
Where the midday glows under its burning rays,
Where the Great Bear freezes the surface of the sea;
And since thou, mightiest of mighty kings, dost order
That mild laws should prevail according to thy will;
Therefore to thee in a spirit of loyalty this world map
    has been dedicated
By him who has prepared it with wonderful skill.

THE END.

PREFACE

TO HIS MAJESTY
MAXIMILIAN CÆSAR AUGUSTUS
MARTINUS ILACOMILUS WISHES
GOOD FORTUNE

IF it is not only pleasant but also profitable
in life to visit many lands and to see the most
distant races (a fact that is made clear in Plato,
Apollonius of Tyana, and many other philosophers, who went to the most remote regions
for the purpose of exploration), who, I ask,
most invincible Maximilian Cæsar, will deny
that it is pleasant and profitable to learn from
books the location of lands and cities and of
foreign peoples,

> Which Phœbus sees when he buries his rays be-
> neath the waves,
> Which he sees as he comes from the farthest east,
> Which the cold northern stars distress,
> Which the south wind parches with its torrid heat,
> Baking again the burning sands?
>
> (Boethius.)

Who, I repeat, will deny that it is pleasant and
profitable to learn from books the manners and

33

customs of all these peoples? Surely—to express my own opinion—just as it is worthy of praise to travel far, so it can not be foolish for one who knows the world, even from maps alone, to repeat again and again that passage of the Odyssey which Homer, the most learned of poets, wrote about Ulysses:

> Tell me, O Muse, of the man who after the capture of Troy
> Saw the customs and the cities of many men.

Therefore, studying, to the best of my ability and with the aid of several persons, the books of Ptolemy from a Greek copy, and adding the relations of the four voyages of Amerigo Vespucci, I have prepared for the general use of scholars a map of the whole world—like an introduction, so to speak—both in the solid and projected on the plane. This work I have determined to dedicate to your most sacred Majesty, since you are the lord of the world, feeling certain that I shall accomplish my end and shall be safe from the intrigues of my enemies under your protecting shield, as though under that of Achilles, if I know that I have satisfied, to some extent at least, your Majesty's keen judgment in such matters. Farewell, most illustrious Cæsar.

At St. Dié, in the year 1507 after the birth of Our Saviour.

ORDER OF TREATMENT

SINCE no one can obtain a thorough knowledge of Cosmography without some previous understanding of astronomy, nor even of astronomy itself without the principles of geometry, we shall in this brief outline say a few words:

(1) Of the elements of geometry that will be helpful to a better understanding of the material sphere;

(2) Of the meaning of *sphere, axis, poles,* etc.;

(3) Of the circles of the heavens;

(4) Of a certain theory, which we shall propose, of the sphere itself according to the system of degrees;

(5) Of the five celestial zones, and the application of these and of the degrees of the heavens to the earth;

(6) Of parallels;

(7) Of the climates[1] of the earth;

(8) Of winds, with a general diagram of these and other things;

(9) Of the divisions of the earth, of the various seas, of islands, and of the distances of

[1] The word *climate* is here used in its ancient sense of a zone of the earth's surface comprised between two specified parallels of latitude.

places from one another.   There will be added also a quadrant useful to the cosmographer.

Lastly, we shall add the four voyages of Amerigo Vespucci.   Thus we shall describe the cosmography, both in the solid and projected on the plane.

CHAPTER I

Of the Principles of Geometry Necessary to an Understanding of the Sphere

Since in the following pages frequent mention will be made of the circle, the circumference, the center, the diameter, and other similar terms, we ought first of all briefly to discuss these terms one by one.

A circle is a plane figure bounded by a line drawn around, and in the middle there is a point, all straight lines drawn from which to the surrounding line are equal to one another.

A plane figure is a figure, no point of which rises above or falls below the lines that bound it.

The circumference is the line that so bounds the circle that all straight lines drawn from the center to the circumference are equal to one another. The circumference is also called in Latin *ambitus, circuitus, curvatura, circulus,* and in Greek *periphereia.*

The center of a circle is a point so situated that all straight lines drawn from it to the line bounding the circle are equal to one another.

A semicircle is a plane figure bounded by the

diameter of the circle and one half of the circumference.

The diameter of a circle is any straight line passing through the center of the circle and extending in both directions to the circumference.

A straight line is the shortest distance between two points.

An angle is the mutual coming together of two lines. It is the portion of a figure increasing in width from the point of intersection.

A right angle is an angle formed by one line falling upon another line and making the two angles on either side equal to each other. If a right angle is bounded by straight lines, it is called plane; if bounded by curved lines, it is called curved or spherical.

An obtuse angle is an angle that is greater than a right angle.

An acute angle is less than a right angle.

A solid is a body measured by length, breadth, and height.

Height, thickness, and depth are the same.

A degree is a whole thing or part of a thing which is not the result of a division into sixtieths.

A minute is the sixtieth part of a degree.

A second is the sixtieth part of a minute.

A third is the sixtieth part of a second, and so on.

CHAPTER II

Sᴘʜᴇʀᴇ, Axɪꜱ, Pᴏʟᴇꜱ, Eᴛᴄ., Aᴄᴄᴜʀᴀᴛᴇʟʏ
Dᴇꜰɪɴᴇᴅ

Bᴇꜰᴏʀᴇ any one can obtain a knowledge of
cosmography, it is necessary that he should
have an understanding of the material sphere.
After that he will more easily comprehend the
description of the entire world which was first
handed down by Ptolemy and others and afterward enlarged by later scholars, and on which
further light has recently been thrown by
Amerigo Vespucci.

A sphere, as Theodosius defines it in his book
on spheres, is a solid and material figure bounded
by a convex surface, in the center of which
there is a point, all straight lines drawn from
which to the circumference are equal to one
another. And while, according to modern
writers, there are ten celestial spheres, there is
a material sphere like the eighth (which is
called the fixed sphere because it carries the
fixed stars), composed of circles joined together
ideally by a line and axis crossing the center,
that is, the earth.

The axis of a sphere is a line passing through

the center and touching with its extremities the circumference of the sphere on both sides. About this axis the sphere whirls and turns like the wheel of a wagon about its axle, which is a smoothly rounded pole, the axis being the diameter of the circle itself. Of this Manilius speaks as follows:

> Through the cold air a slender line is drawn,
> Round which the starry world revolves.

The poles, which are also called *cardines* (hinges) and *vertices* (tops), are the points of the heavens terminating the axis, so fixed that they never move, but always remain in the same place. What is said here about the axis and the poles is to be referred to the eighth sphere, since for the present we have undertaken the limitation of the material sphere, which, as we have said, resembles the eighth sphere. There are accordingly two principal poles, one the northern, also called *Arcticus* (arctic) and *Borealis* (of Boreas), the other the southern, also called *Antarcticus* (antarctic). Of these Vergil says:

The one pole is always above us, but the other
The black Styx and the deep shades see 'neath our feet.

We who live in Europe and Asia see the arctic pole always. It is so called from *Arctus*, or *Arcturus*, the Great Bear, which is also named *Calisto*, *Helice*, and *Septentrionalis*, from the seven stars of the Wain, which are called *Triones;* there are seven stars also in the Lesser Bear, sometimes called *Cynosura.* Wherefore Baptista Mantuanus says:

Under thy guidance, Helice, under thine, Cynosura,
We set sail over the deep, etc.

Likewise, the wind coming from that part of the world is called *Borealis* and *Aquilonicus* (northern). Sailors are accustomed to call *Cynosura* the star of the sea.

Opposite to the arctic pole is the antarctic, whence it derives its name, for ἀντί in Greek is the equivalent of *contra* in Latin. This pole is also called *Noticus* and *Austronoticus* (southern). It can not be seen by us on account of the curvature of the earth, which slopes downward, but is visible from the antipodes (the existence of which has been established). It should be remarked in passing that the downward slope of a spherical object means its swelling or belly; that convexity is the contrary of it and denotes concavity.

There are, besides, two other poles of the zodiac itself, describing two circles in the heavens, the arctic and the antarctic. Since we have made mention of the zodiac, the arctic, and the antarctic (which are circles in the heavens), we shall treat of circles in the following chapter.

CHAPTER III

Of the Circles of the Heavens

THERE are two kinds of circles, called also *segmina* by authors, on the sphere and in the heavens, not really existing, but imaginary; namely, great and small circles.

A great circle is one which, described on the convex surface of the sphere, divides it into two equal parts. There are six great circles: the equator, the zodiac, the equinoctial colure, the solstitial colure, the meridian, the horizon.

A small circle on the sphere is one which, described on the same surface of the sphere, divides it into two unequal parts. There are four small circles: the arctic, the circle of Cancer, the circle of Capricorn, the antarctic. Thus there are in all ten, of which we shall speak in order, first of the great circles.

The equator, which is also called the girdle of the *primum mobile* and the equinoctial, is a great circle dividing the sphere into two equal parts. Any point of the equator is equally distant from both poles. It is so called because, when the sun crosses it (which happens twice a year, at the first point of Aries, in the month of March, and at the first point of Libra, in the month of September), it is the equinox throughout the world and the day and night are equal. The equinox of March or of Aries is the vernal equinox, the equinox of September or of Libra the autumnal.

The zodiac is a great circle intersecting the equator at two points, which are the first points of Aries and Libra. One half of it inclines to the north, the other to the south. It is so called either from ζῴδιον, meaning an *animal*, because it has twelve animals in it, or from ζωή, meaning *life*, because it is understood that the lives of all the lower animals are governed by the movements of the planets. The Latins call it *signifer* (sign-bearing), because it has twelve signs in it, and the oblique circle. Therefore Vergil says:

Where the series of the signs might revolve obliquely.

In the middle of the width of the zodiac there is a circular line dividing it into two equal parts and leaving six degrees of latitude on either side. This line is called the ecliptic, because no eclipse of the sun or moon ever takes place unless both of them pass under that line in the same or in opposite degrees,—in the same, if it is to be an eclipse of the sun; in opposite, if it is to be an eclipse of the moon. The sun always passes with its center under that line and never deviates from it. The moon and the rest of the planets wander at one time under the line, at another on one side or the other.

There are two colures on the sphere, which are distinguished as solstitial and equinoctial. They are so called from the Greek κῶλον, which means a *member* and the Latin *uri boves* (wild oxen), which Cæsar says, in the fourth book' of his "Commentaries," are found in the Hercynian forest and are of the size of elephants, because, just as the tail of an ox when raised makes a semicircular and incomplete member, so the colure always appears to us incomplete, for one half is visible, while the other half is concealed.

The solstitial colure, which is also called the circle of declinations, is a great circle passing through the first points of Cancer and Capricorn, as well as through the poles of the ecliptic and the poles of the world.

The equinoctial colure, in like manner, is a great circle passing through the first points of Aries and Libra and the poles of the world.

The meridian is a great circle passing through

The passage referred to is in the sixth book, chapter xxviii, of the Commentaries.

the point vertically overhead and the poles of the world. These circles we have drawn ten degrees apart in our world map in the solid and projected on the plane. There is a point in the heavens directly over any object, which is called the zenith.

The horizon, also called *finitor* (limiting line), is a great circle of the sphere dividing the upper hemisphere (that is, the half of a sphere) from the lower. It is the circle at which the vision of those who stand under the open sky and cast their eyes about seems to end. It appears to separate the part of the heavens that is seen from the part that is not seen. The horizon of different places varies, and the point vertically overhead of every horizon is called the pole, for such a point is equally distant in all directions from the *finitor* or the horizon itself.

Having thus considered the great circles, let us now proce d to the small circles.

The arctic circle is a small circle which one pole of the zodiac describes about the arctic pole of the world by the motion of the *primum mobile*.

The antarctic is a small circle which the other pole of the zodiac makes and describes about the antarctic pole of the world. We mean by the pole of the zodiac (of which we spoke also in the preceding chapter), the point that is equally distant from any point on the ecliptic, for the poles of the zodiac are the extremities of the axis of the ecliptic. The distance of the pole of the zodiac from the pole of the world is equal to the greatest declination of the sun (of which we shall say more presently).

The tropic of Cancer is a small circle which the sun, when at the first point of Cancer, describes by the motion of the *primum mobile*. This point is also called the summer solstice.

The tropic of Capricorn is a small circle which the sun, when at the first point of Capricorn, describes by the motion of the *primum mobile*. This circle is also called the circle of the winter solstice.

Since we have mentioned declination, it should be remarked that declination occurs when the sun descends from the equinoctial to the tropic of Cancer, or from us to the tropic of Capricorn; that ascension, on the contrary, occurs when the sun approaches the equator from the tropics. It is, however, improperly said by some that the sun ascends when it approaches us and descends when it goes away from us.

Thus far we have spoken of circles. Let us now proceed to the theory of the sphere and a fuller consideration of the degrees by which such circles are distant from one another.

CHAPTER IV

OF A CERTAIN THEORY OF THE SPHERE ACCORDING TO THE SYSTEM OF DEGREES

THE celestial sphere is surrounded by five principal circles, one great and four small—the arctic, the circle of Cancer, the equator, the circle of Capricorn, and the antarctic. Of these the equator is a great circle, the other four are small circles. These circles, or rather the spaces tnat are between them, authors are wont to call zones. Thus Vergil, in the Georgics, says:

Five zones the heavens contain ; whereof is one
Aye red with flashing sunlight, fervent aye
From fire ; on either side to left and right
Are traced the utmost twain, stiff with blue ice,
And black with scowling storm-clouds, and betwixt
These and the midmost, other twain there lie,
By the gods' grace to heart-sick mortals given,
And a path cleft between them, where might wheel
On sloping plane the system of the signs.

Of the nature of the zones more will be said in the following pages. Inasmuch as we have mentioned above the pole of the zodiac that describes the arctic circle, therefore in place of further consideration this must be understood to mean the upper pole of the zodiac (situated at an elevation of 66° 9′, and distant from the arctic pole 24° 51″[1]). It must be recalled also that a degree is the thirtieth part of a sign, that a sign is the twelfth part of a circle, and that thirty multiplied by twelve gives three hundred and sixty. So it becomes clear that a degree can be defined as the three hundred and sixtieth part of a circle.

The lower pole of the zodiac describes the antarctic circle, which is situated in the same degree of declination and is at the same distance from the antarctic pole as the upper pole of the zodiac is from the arctic. The inclination of the ecliptic, or the greatest declination of the sun toward the north (which is situated 33° 51″[2] from the equinoctial), describes the tropic of Cancer.

The other inclination of the ecliptic, or the greatest declination of the sun toward the south (which is situated the same number of degrees as stated before), describes the tropic of Capricorn.

The distance between the tropic of Cancer and the arctic circle is 42° 18′. The distance between the tropic of Capricorn and the antarctic circle is the same.

The middle of the heavens, being equally distant from the poles of the world, makes the equator.

[1] Error for 23° 51′. [2] Error for 23° 51′.

Hitherto we have spoken of the five zones and of their distance from one another. We shall now briefly discuss the remaining circles.

The circle of the zodiac is determined by the poles of the zodiac. From the poles to the tropics (that is, to the greatest declinations of the sun or the solstices), the distance is 42° 18'. The width of the zodiac from the ecliptic toward either of the tropics is 6°, or in all 12°.

The solstices and the equinoxes mark the colures of declination and ascension. These intersect under the poles of the world along the axis of the heavens at spherical right angles; likewise along the equator. But the equinoctial colures going along the zodiac make oblique angles, while they make right angles along the zodiac of the solstices. The meridional circle, which is movable, is contained by the same axis under the poles themselves.

The circle of the horizon is determined by the zenith, for, as its upper pole, the zenith is everywhere equally distant from it. The circle of the horizon also divides our hemisphere from the other from east to west, but for those who are beneath the equinoctial, through the two poles of the world. The zenith of every horizon is always distant 90°, which is the fourth part of a circle, from the circumference of the horizon, while the circumference of the horizon is four times as great as the distance between the zenith and the horizon.

It is worthy of notice that the axis of the world in the material sphere passes diametrically from the poles through the center of the world, which is the earth.

The axis of the zodiac, however, is not apparent in the sphere, but has to be conceived. This intersects the middle of the axis of the world, making unequal or oblique angles at the center.

In this way, in the very creation of the world there seems to be a wonderful order and extraordinary arrangement. The old astronomers, in describing the form of the world, followed, as far as possible, in the footsteps of the Creator Himself, who made all things according to number, weight, and dimensions. We, too, while treating of this subject, inasmuch as we are so hampered by the conditions of our space that our system of minutes can be perceived only with difficulty, or not at all, and, if perceived, would beget even annoyance as well as error, shall infer the positions of circles from the markings of degrees in full. For there is not much difference between 51′ and a full degree, which contains 60′, as we have said before, and in the book on the sphere and elsewhere it is indicated in exactly this way by specialists on this subject. Therefore in the diagram which we shall here insert for the better understanding of these matters, the tropics of Cancer and Capricorn and the greatest declinations of the sun will be distant 24° from the equinoctial, the same as the distance of the poles of the zodiac or the arctic and antarctic circles from the poles of the world, situated at an elevation of over 66°.

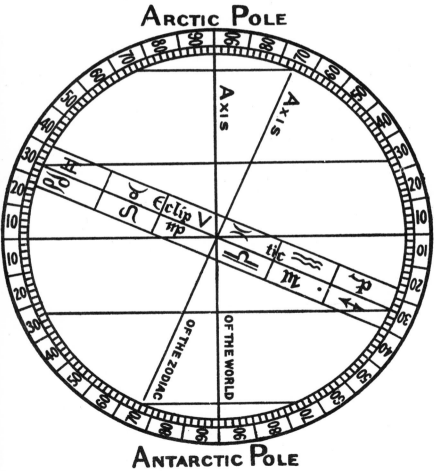

CHAPTER V

OF THE FIVE CELESTIAL ZONES AND THE APPLICATION OF THESE AND OF THE DEGREES OF THE HEAVENS TO THE EARTH

UP TO this point we have spoken very briefly of several geometrical principles, of the sphere, the poles, the five zones, the circles of the world, and of a certain theory in regard to these matters. Now, in regular order, if I am not mistaken, we come to the consideration of the application of these circles and degrees to the earth. It should therefore be known that on the earth there are five regions corresponding to the above-mentioned zones. Wherefore Ovid in the *Metamorphoses* says:

And as two zones the northern heaven restrain,
The southern two, and one the hotter midst,
With five the Godhead girt th' inclosed earth,
And climates five upon its face imprest.
The midst from heat inhabitable : snows
Eternal cover two : 'twixt these extremes
Two temperate regions lie, where heat and cold
Meet in due mixture.

(Metamorphoses, i, 45–51, translated by Howard.)

In order to make the matter clearer, let us

state that the four small circles, the arctic, the circle of Cancer, the circle of Capricorn, and the antarctic, divide and separate the five zones of the heavens.

In the following diagram let *a* represent the arctic pole of the world, *bc* the arctic circle, *de* the circle of Cancer, *fg* the circle of Capricorn, *hk* the antarctic circle, and *l* the south pole.

The first zone, or the arctic, is all the space included between *bac*. This zone, being frozen stiff with perpetual cold, is uninhabited.

The second zone is all the space included between *bc* and *de*. This is a temperate zone and is habitable.

The third zone is all the space included between *de* and *fg*. This zone, on account of its heat, is scarcely habitable; for the sun, describing circles there with a constant whirling motion along the line *fe* (which for us marks the ecliptic), by reason of its heat makes the zone torrid and uninhabited.

The fourth zone is all the space included between *fg* and *hk*. This is a temperate zone and is habitable, if the immense areas of water and the changed conditions of the atmosphere permit it.

The fifth zone is all the space included between *hkl*. This zone is always stiff with cold and uninhabited.

When we say that any zone of the heavens is either inhabited or uninhabited, we wish it to be understood that this applies to the corresponding zone lying beneath that celestial zone. When we say that any zone is inhabited or inhabitable, we mean that it is easily inhabitable. Likewise, when we say that any zone is uninhabited or uninhabitable, we understand that it is habitable with difficulty. For there are many people who now inhabit the dried-up torrid zone, such as the inhabitants of the Golden Chersonese,[1] the Taprobanenses,[2] the Ethiopians, and a very large part of the earth which had always been unknown, but which has recently been discovered by Amerigo Vespucci. In this connection we may state that we shall add the four voyages of Vespucci, translated from the Italian language into French and from French into Latin.

It must be understood, as the following diagram shows, that the first zone, which is nearest to the arctic pole, is 23° 51′ in extent; the second, which is the antarctic, is equal to the arctic, and is therefore the same in extent; the third, a temperate zone, is 42° 18′; the fourth, which is equal to it, is also 42° 18′; the fifth, which is the torrid and is in the middle, is 47° 42′.

[1] The peninsula of Malacca in India is probably meant.
[2] The people of what is now the island of Ceylon.

Let us here insert the diagram.

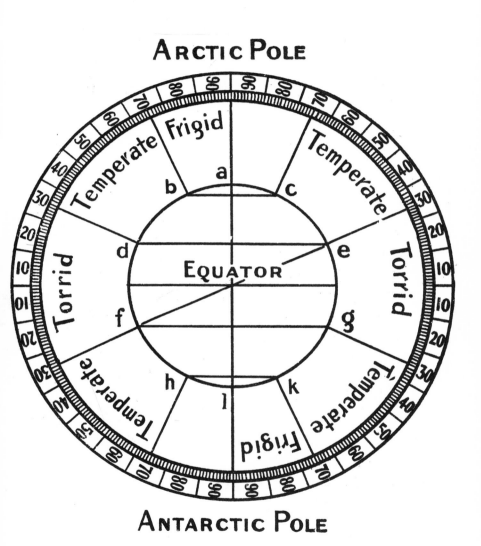

CHAPTER VI

OF PARALLELS

PARALLELS, which are also called Almucantars, are circles or lines equidistant in every direction and at every point, and never running together even if extended to infinity. They bear the same relation to one another as the equator does to the four small circles on the sphere, not that the second is as distant from the third as the first is from the second, for this is false, as is clear from the preceding pages, but that any two circles joined together by a perpendicular are equally distant from each other throughout their extent. For the equator is neither nearer to nor more distant from one of the tropics at any one point than at any other, since it is everywhere distant 23° 51' from the tropics, as we have said before. The same must be said of the distance from the tropics to the two extreme circles, either of which is distant 42° 44" from the nearer tropic at all points.

Although parallels can be drawn at any distance apart, yet, to make the reckoning easier,

¹ Error for 42° 18'.

it has seemed to us most convenient, as it seemed to Ptolemy also, in our representation of universal cosmography, both in the solid and projected on the plane, to separate the parallels by as many degrees from one another as the following table shows. To this table a diagram also will be subjoined, in which we shall extend the parallels through the earth on both sides to the celestial sphere.

Of Parallels

Parallels from the equator	Degrees of the heavens	Greatest number of hours in a day	Number of miles in one degree
21 Of Thule 8	63	20	$28\frac{1}{2}$
20	61	19	
19	58	18	$32\frac{1}{2}$
18	56	17	$\frac{1}{2}$ (*sic ?*)
17	54	17	$37\frac{1}{2}$
16 Of the Rhiphæan Mts. 7	$51\frac{1}{2}$	$16\frac{1}{2}$	$40\frac{1}{2}$
15 Of the Borysthenes (Dnieper) 6	$48\frac{1}{2}$	16	$42\frac{1}{2}$
14	45	$15\frac{1}{2}$	44
13	$43\frac{1}{12}$	$15\frac{1}{4}$	45
12 Of Rome 5	$40\frac{11}{12}$	15	47
11	$38\frac{7}{12}$	$14\frac{3}{4}$	$48\frac{1}{2}$
10 Of Rhodes 4	36	$14\frac{1}{2}$	50
9	$33\frac{1}{3}$	$14\frac{1}{4}$	
8 Of Alexandria 3	$30\frac{1}{3}$	14	54
7	$27\frac{2}{3}$	$13\frac{3}{4}$	
6 Of Syene 2	$23\frac{5}{6}$	$13\frac{1}{2}$	57
5	$20\frac{1}{4}$	$13\frac{1}{4}$	
4 Of Meroe 1	$16\frac{5}{12}$	13	
3	$12\frac{1}{2}$	$12\frac{3}{4}$	
2	$8\frac{5}{12}$	$12\frac{1}{2}$	
1	$4\frac{1}{4}$	$12\frac{1}{4}$	59
Equator equidistant from the poles		12 always	60
1	$4\frac{1}{4}$	$12\frac{1}{4}$	59
2	$8\frac{5}{12}$	$12\frac{1}{2}$	
3	$12\frac{1}{2}$	$12\frac{3}{4}$	
4 Anti-climate of Meroe	$16\frac{5}{12}$	13	
5	$20\frac{1}{4}$	$13\frac{1}{4}$	

This diagram shows by its numbers the climates, the degrees of the parallels, and the hours.

Parallels & Climates	Degrees	Hours	Miles
6 Anti-Climate of Syene	$23\frac{5}{6}$	$13\frac{1}{2}$	52
7	$27\frac{2}{3}$	$13\frac{3}{4}$	

And so on toward the Antarctic Pole, as the following diagram shows:

ARCTIC POLE

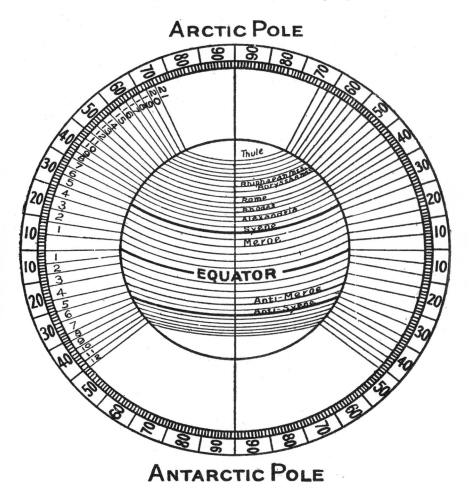

ANTARCTIC POLE

CHAPTER VII

OF CLIMATES

ALTHOUGH the word *climate* properly means a region, it is here used to mean a part of the earth between two equidistant parallels, in which from the beginning to the end of the climate there is a difference of a half-hour in the longest day. The number of any climate, reckoned from the equator, indicates the number of half-hours by which the longest day in that climate exceeds the day that is equal to the night. There are seven of these climates, although to the south the seventh has not yet been explored. But toward the north Ptolemy discovered a country that was hospitable and habitable, at a distance represented by seven half-hours. These seven climates have obtained their names from some prominent city, river, or mountain.

1. The first climate is called Dia Meroes (of Meroe, modern Shendi), from διά, which in Greek means *through* and governs the genitive case, and Meroe, which is a city of Africa situated in the torrid zone 16° on this side of the equator, in the same parallel in which the Nile is found. Our world map, for the better understanding of which this is written, will clearly

show you the beginning, the middle, and the end of this first climate and also of the rest, as well as the hours of the longest day in every one of them.

2. Dia Sienes (of Syene, modern Assuan), from Syene, a city of Egypt, the beginning of the province of Thebais.

3. Dia Alexandrias (of Alexandria), from Alexandria, a famous city of Africa, the chief city of Egypt, founded by Alexander the Great, of whom it has been said by the poet:

One world is not enough for the youth of Pella.[1]
—(Juvenal, x, 168.)

4. Dia Rhodon (of Rhodes), from Rhodes, an island on the coast of Asia Minor, on which in our time there is situated a famous city of the same name, which bravely resisted the fierce and warlike attacks of the Turks and gloriously defeated them.

5. Dia Rhomes (of Rome), from a well-known city of Europe, the most illustrious among the cities of Italy and at one time the famous conqueror of all nations and the capital of the world. It is now the abode of the great Father of Fathers.

6. Dia Borysthenes (of Borysthenes, modern Dnieper), from a large river of the Scythians, the fourth from the Danube.

[1] A city in Macedonia, the birthplace of Alexander.

7. Dia Rhipheon (of the Rhiphæan Mountains), from the Rhiphæan mountains, a prominent range in Sarmatian Europe, white with perpetual snow.

From these prominent places, through which approximately the median lines of the climates pass, the seven climates established by Ptolemy derive their names.

The eighth climate Ptolemy did not locate, because that part of the earth, whatever it is, was unknown to him, but was explored by later scholars. It is called Dia Tyles (of Thule, modern Iceland or Shetland), because the beginning of the climate, which is the twenty-first parallel from the equator, passes directly through Thule. Thule is an island in the north, of which our poet Vergil says:

The farthest Thule will serve.

—(Georgics, i, 30.)

So much for the climates north of the equator. In like manner we must speak of those which are south of the equator, six of which having corresponding names have been explored and may be called Antidia Meroes (Anti-climate of Meroe), Antidia Alexandrias, Antidia Rhodon, Antidia Rhomes, Antidia Borysthenes, from the Greek particle αντί, which means *opposite* or *against*. In the sixth climate toward the antarctic there are situated the farthest part of Africa, recently discovered, the islands Zanzibar, the lesser Java, and Seula (Sumatra ?), and the fourth part of the earth, which, because Amerigo discovered it, we may call Amerige, the land of Amerigo, so to speak, or America. It is of these southern climates that these words of Pomponius Mela, the geographer, must be understood, when he says:

The habitable zones have the same seasons, but at different times of the year. The Antichthones inhabit the one, and we the other. The situation of the former zone being unknown to us on account of the heat of the intervening zone, I can speak only of the situation of the latter.   —(Perieg. i, 1, 9.)

Here it should be remarked that each one of the climates generally bears products different from any other, inasmuch as the climates are different in character and are controlled by different influences of the stars. Wherefore Vergil says :

Nor can all climes all fruits of earth produce.
 *   *   *   *   *   *   *
Here blithelier springs the corn, and here the grape,
Their earth is green with tender growth of trees
And grass unbidden. See how from Tmolus comes
The saffron's fragrance, ivory from Ind,
From Saba's weakling sons their frankincense,
Iron from the naked Chalybs, castor rank
From Pontus, from Epirus the prize-palms
O' the mares of Elis.
          —(Georgics, i, 54-59, translated by Rhoades.)

CHAPTER VIII
Of the Winds

SINCE in the preceding pages we have mentioned the winds now and then (when we spoke of the north pole, the south pole, etc.), and as it is understood that a knowledge of winds is of some importance, or rather of great advantage, to cosmography, we shall for these reasons say something in this chapter about winds, also called *spiritus* and *flatus* (breeze). A wind, therefore, as defined by the philosophers, is an exhalation, warm and dry, moving laterally around the earth, etc.

Now, inasmuch as the sun has a triple rising and setting, the summer rising and setting, the equinoctial rising and setting, and the winter rising and setting, according to its relation to the two tropics and the equator, and inasmuch as there are also two sides—to the north and to the south, all of which have winds peculiar to them ; therefore it follows that there are twelve winds in all, three eastern, three western, three northern, and three southern. Of these the four which in the following diagram occupy the middle place are the principal winds; the others are secondary.

		East	West
Side	Tropic of Cancer	Kaikias	Chorus
Principal	Equator	Subsolanus	Favonius or Zephyrus
Side	Tropic of Capricorn	Eurus or Vulturnus	Africus or Libs

		South	North
Side		Euronotus	Septentrio
Principal		Auster or Notus	Aquilo or Boreas
Side		Libonotus	Trachias or Circius

The poets, however, by poetic license, according to their custom, instead of the principal winds use their secondary winds, which are also called side winds. Thus Ovid says:

> Far to the east
> Where Persian mountains greet the rising sun
> Eurus withdrew. Where sinking Phœbus' rays
> Glow on the western shores mild Zephyr fled.
> Terrific Boreas frozen Scythia seiz'd,
> Beneath the icy bear. On southern climes
> From constant clouds the showery Auster rains.
> —(Metamorphoses, i, 61-66, translated by Howard.)

65

The east wind (Subsolanus), which is rendered by the sun purer and finer than the others, is very healthful.

The west wind (Zephyrus), having a mixture of heat and moisture, melts the snows. Whence Vergil's verse :

Melts from the mountain's hoar, and Zephyr's breath
Unbinds the crumbling clod.

—(Georgics, i, 44, translated by Rhoades.)

The south wind (Auster) frequently presages storms, hurricanes, and showers. Wherefore Ovid says :

Notus rushes forth
On pinions dropping rain.

—(Metamorphoses, i, 264, translated by Howard.)

The north wind (Aquilo), by reason of the severity of its cold, freezes the waters.

And frosty winter with his north the sea's face rough doth wear.

—(Vergil, Æneid, iii, 285, translated by Morris.)

In regard to these winds, I remember, our poet Gallinarius, a man of great learning, composed the following :

Eurus and Subsolanus blow from the east.
Zephyrus and Favonius fill the west with breezes.
Auster and Notus rage on Libya's farthest shores.
Boreas and Aquilo cloud-dispelling threaten from the north.

Although the north winds are naturally cold, they are softened because they pass through the torrid zone. This has been found to be true of the south wind, which passes through the torrid zone before it reaches us, as is shown in the following lines :

Wherever the cold south wind goes, it rages and binds the waters with tight fetters. But until with its blast it passes through the torrid regions, it comes welcome to our shores and hurls back the merciless shafts of the north wind. The latter wind on the contrary, which deals harshly with us, slackening its flight, becomes in like manner gentler in the lowest part of the globe. The other winds, where they direct their various courses, soon change, as they go, the natures which are proper to their homes.

We have said enough about winds. We shall now insert a general map, indicating the poles, the axes, the circles, great as well as small, the east, the west, the five zones, the degrees of longitude and latitude, both on the earth and in the heavens, the parallels, the climates, the winds, etc.

THE purpose of this little book is to write a description of the world map, which we have designed, both as a globe and as a projection. The globe I have designed on a small scale, the map on a larger. As farmers usually mark off and divide their farms by boundary lines, so it has been our endeavor to mark the chief countries of the world by the emblems of their rulers. And (to begin with our own continent) in the middle of Europe we have placed the eagles of the Roman Empire (which rule the kings of Europe), and with the key (which is the symbol of the Holy Father) we have enclosed almost the whole of Europe, which acknowledges the Roman Church. The greater part of Africa and a part of Asia we have distinguished by crescents, which are the emblems of the supreme Sultan of Babylonia, the lord of all Egypt, and of a part of Asia. The part of Asia called Asia Minor we have surrounded with a saffron-colored cross joined to a branding iron, which is the symbol of the Sultan of the Turks, who rules Scythia this side of the Imaus, the highest mountains of Asia and Sarmatian Scythia. Asiatic Scythia we have marked by anchors, which are the emblems of the great Tartar Khan. A red cross symbolizes Prester John (who rules both eastern and southern India and who resides in Biberith); and finally on the fourth division of the earth, discovered by the kings of Castile and Portugal, we have placed the emblems of those sovereigns. And what is to be borne in mind, we have marked with crosses shallow places in the sea where shipwreck may be feared. Herewith we close.

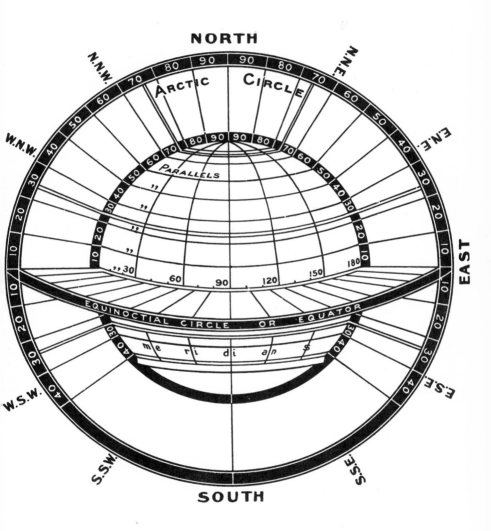

CHAPTER IX

OF CERTAIN ELEMENTS OF COSMOGRAPHY

IT is clear from astronomical demonstrations that the whole earth is a point in comparison with the entire extent of the heavens; so that if the earth's circumference be compared to the size of the celestial globe, it may be considered to have absolutely no extent. There is about a fourth part of this small region in the world which was known to Ptolemy and is inhabited by living beings like ourselves. Hitherto it has been divided into three parts, Europe, Africa, and Asia.

Europe is bounded on the west by the Atlantic Ocean, on the north by the British Ocean, on the east by the river Tanais (modern Don), Lake Maeotis (modern Sea of Azov), and the Black Sea, and on the south by the Mediterranean Sea. It includes Spain, Gaul, Germany, Rætia, Italy, Greece, and Sarmatia. Europe is so called after Europa, the daughter of King Agenor. While with a girl's enthusiasm she was playing on the sea-shore accompanied by her Tyrian maidens and was gathering flowers in baskets, she is believed to have been carried off by

Jupiter, who assumed the form of a snow-white bull, and after being brought over the seas to Crete seated upon his back to have given her name to the land lying opposite.

Africa is bounded on the west by the Atlantic Ocean, on the south by the Ethiopian Ocean, on the north by the Mediterranean Sea, and on the east by the river Nile. It embraces the Mauritanias, viz., Tingitana (modern Tangiers) and Cæsarea,, inland Libya, Numidia (also called Mapalia), lesser Africa (in which is Carthage, formerly the constant rival of the Roman empire), Cyrenaica, Marmarica (modern Barca), Libya (by which name also the whole of Africa is called, from Libs, a king of Mauritania), inland Ethiopia, Egypt, etc. It is called Africa because it is free from the severity of the cold.

Asia, which far surpasses the other divisions in size and in resources, is separated from Europe by the river Tanais (Don) ·and from Africa by the Isthmus, which stretching southward divides the Arabian and the Egyptian seas. The principal countries of Asia are Bithynia, Galatia, Cappadocia, Pamphylia, Lydia, Cilicia, greater and lesser Armenia, Colchis, Hyrcania, Iberia, and Albania; besides many other countries which it would only delay us to enumerate one by one. Asia is so called after a queen of that name.

Now, these parts of the earth have been more extensively explored and a fourth part has been discovered by Amerigo Vespucci (as will be set forth in what follows). Inasmuch as both Europe and Asia received their names from women, I see no reason why any one should justly object to calling this part Amerige, i.e., the land of Amerigo, or America, after Amerigo, its discoverer, a man of great ability. Its position and the customs of its inhabitants may be clearly understood from the four voyages of Amerigo, which are subjoined.

Thus the earth is now known to be divided into four parts. The first three parts are continents, while the fourth is an island, inasmuch as it is found to be surrounded on all sides by the ocean. Although there is only one ocean, just as there is only one earth, yet, being marked by many seas and filled with numberless islands, it takes various names. These names may be found in the Cosmography, and Priscian in his translation of Dionysius enumerates them in the following lines:

"The vast abyss of the ocean, however, surrounds the earth on every side; but the ocean, although there is only one, takes many names. In the western countries it is called the Atlantic Ocean, but in the north, where the Arimaspi are ever warring, it is called the sluggish sea, the Saturnian Sea, and by others the Dead Sea,

* * * * * * *

Where, however, the sun rises with its first light, they call it the Eastern or the Indian Sea. But where the inclined pole receives the burning south wind, it is called the Ethiopian or the Red Sea,

* * * * * * *

Thus the great ocean, known under various names, encircles the whole world;

* * * * * * *

"Of its arms the first that stretches out breaks through Spain with its waves, and extends from the shores of Libya to the coast of Pamphylia. This is smaller than the rest. A larger gulf is the one that enters into the Caspian land, which receives it from the vast waters of the north. The arm of the sea which Tethys (the ocean) rules as the Saturnian Sea is called the Caspian or the Hyrcanian. But of the two gulfs that come from the south sea, one, the Persian, running northward, forms a deep sea, lying opposite the country where the Caspian waves roll; while the other rolls and beats the shores of Panchæa and extends to the south opposite to the Euxine Sea.

* * * * * * *

"Let us begin in regular order with the waters of the Atlantic, which Cadiz makes

famous by Hercules' gift of the pillar, where
Atlas, standing on a mountain, holds up the
columns that support the heavens. The first
sea is the Iberian, which separates Europe from
Libya, washing the shores of both. On either
side are the pillars. Both face the shores, the
one looking toward Libya, the other toward
Europe. Then comes the Gallic Sea, which
beats the Celtic shores. After this the sea,
called by the name of the Ligurians, where the
masters of the world grew up on Latin soil, extends from the north to Leucopetra; where the
island of Sicily with its curving shore forms a
strait. Cyrnos (modern Corsica) is washed by
the waters that bear its name and flow between
the Sardinian Sea and the Celtic. Then rolls
the surging tide of the Tyrrhenian Sea, turning
toward the south; it enters the sea of Sicily,
which turns toward the east and spreading far
from the shores of Pachynum extends to Crete,
a steep rock, which stands out of the sea, where
powerful Gortyna and Phæstum are situated in the
midst of the fields. This rock, resembling with
its peak the forehead of a ram, the Greeks have
justly called $K\rho\iota o\tilde{\upsilon}$ $\mu\acute{\epsilon}\tau\omega\pi o\nu$ (ram's forehead). The
sea of Sicily ends at Mt. Garganus on the coast
of Apulia.

"Beginning there the vast Adriatic extends
toward the northwest. There also is the Ionian

Sea, famous throughout the world. It separates two shores, which, however, meet in one point. On the right fertile Illyria extends, and next to this the land of the warlike Dalmatians. But its left is bounded by the Ausonian peninsula, whose curving shores the three seas, the Tyrrhenian, the Sicilian, and the vast Adriatic, encircle on all sides. Each of these seas within its limits has a wind peculiar to itself. The west wind lashes the Tyrrhenian, the south wind the Sicilian, while the east wind breaks the waters of the Adriatic which roll beneath its blasts.

" Leaving Sicily the sea spreads its deep expanse to the greater Syrtis which the coast of Libya encircles. After the greater Syrtis passes into the lesser, the two seas beat far and wide upon the re-echoing shores. From Sicily the Cretan Sea stretches out toward the east as far as Salmonis, which is said to be the eastern end of Crete.

" Next come two vast seas with dark waves, lashed by the north wind coming from Ismarus, which rushes straight down from the regions of the north. The first, called the Pharian Sea, washes the base of a steep mountain. The second is the Sidonian Sea, which turns toward the north, where the gulf of Issus joins it. This sea does not continue far in a straight line; for it is broken by the shores of Cilicia. Then bending westward it winds like a dragon because, forcing its way through the mountains, it devastates the hills and worries the forests. Its end bounds Pamphylia and surrounds the Chelidonian rocks. Far off to the west it ends near the heights of Patara.

"Next look again toward the north and behold the Ægean Sea, whose waves exceed those of all other seas, and whose vast waters surround the scattered Cyclades. It ends near Imbros and Tenedos, near the narrow strait through which the waters of the Propontis issue, beyond which Asia with its great peoples extends to the south, where the wide peninsula stretches out. Then comes the Thracian Bosporus, the mouth of the Black Sea. In the whole world they say there is no strait narrower than this. There are found the Symplegades, close together. There to the east the Black Sea spreads out, situated in a northeasterly direction. From either side a promontory stands out in the middle of the waters; one, coming from Asia on the south, is called Carambis; the other on the opposite side juts out from the confines of Europe and is called Κριοῦ μέτωπον (ram's forehead.) They face each other, therefore, separated by a sea so wide that a ship can cross it only in three days. Thus you may see the Black Sea looking like a double sea, resembling the curve of a bow, which is bent when the string is drawn tight. The right side resembles the string, for it forms a straight line, outside of which line is found Carambis only, which projects toward the north. But the coast that encloses the sea on the left side, making two turns, describes the arc of the bow. Into this sea toward the north Lake Mæotis (modern Sea of Azov) enters, enclosed on all sides by the land of the Scythians, who call Lake Mæotis the mother of the Black Sea. Indeed, here the violent sea bursts forth in a great stream, rushing across the Cimmerian Bosporus (modern Crimea), in those cold regions where the Cimmerians dwell at the foot of Taurus. Such is the picture of the ocean ; such the glittering appearance of the deep."

(Priscian, Periegesis, 37, foll., ed. of Krehl.)

The sea, as we have said before, is full of islands, of which the largest and the most important, according to Ptolemy, are the following :

Taprobane (modern Ceylon), in the Indian Ocean under the equator ; Albion, also called Britain and England ; Sardinia, in the Mediterranean Sea ; Candia, also called Crete, in the Ægean Sea ; Selandia ; Sicily, in the Mediterranean Sea ; Corsica ; Cyprus.

Unknown to Ptolemy : Madagascar, in the Prasodes Sea ; Zanzibar ; Java, in the East Indian

Ocean; Angama; Peuta, in the Indian Ocean; Seula; Zipangri (Japan), in the Western Ocean.

Of these Priscian says:

"These are the large islands which the waters of the ocean surround. There are many other smaller islands, scattered about in different parts of the world, that are unknown, and that are either difficult of access to hardy sailors or suitable for harbors. Their names I cannot easily express in verse."

(Periegesis, 609-613.)

In order to be able to find out the distance between one place and another, the elevation of the pole must first be considered. It should therefore be briefly remarked that, as is clear from what precedes, both poles are on the horizon for those who live on the parallel of the equator. But as one goes toward the north, the elevation of the pole increases the farther one goes away from the equator. This elevation of the pole indicates the distance of places from the equator. For the distance of any place from the equator varies as the elevation of the pole at that place. From this the number of miles is easily ascertained, if you will multiply the number of degrees of elevation of the pole. But according to Ptolemy, from the equator to the arctic pole miles are not equal in all parts of the world. For any one of the degrees from the first degree of the equator up to the twelfth contains sixty Italian miles, which are equivalent to fifteen German miles, four Italian miles being generally reckoned equal to one German mile. Any degree from the twelfth degree up to the twenty-fifth contains fifty-nine miles, or fourteen and three-quarter German miles.

In order to make the matter clearer, we shall insert the following table :

	Degrees	Degrees	Italian Miles	German Miles
Equator—	1 up to	12 cont'ng	60	15
	12	25	59	14¾
Tropic—	25	30	54	13½
	30	37	50	12½
	37	41	47	11¼ [1]
	41	51	40	10
	51	57	32	8
	57	63	28	7
	63	66	26	6½
Arctic Circle—	66	70	21	5¼
	70	80	6	1½
Arctic Pole—	80	90		0

[1] Error for 11¾.

In like manner from the equator to either arctic or antarctic pole the number of miles in a degree of latitude varies. If you wish to find out the number of miles between one place and another, examine carefully in what degree of latitude the two places are and how many degrees there are between them ; then find out from the above table how many miles there are in a degree of that kind, and multiply this number by the number of degrees between the places. The result will be the number of miles between them. Since these will be Italian miles, divide by four and you will have German miles.

All that has been said by way of introduction to the Cosmography will be sufficient, if we merely advise you that in designing the sheets of our world-map we have not followed Ptolemy in every respect, particularly as regards the new lands, where on the marine charts we observe that the equator is placed otherwise than Ptolemy represented it. Therefore those who notice this ought not to find fault with us, for we have done so purposely, because in this we have followed Ptolemy, and elsewhere the marine charts. Ptolemy himself, in the fifth chapter of his first book, says that he was not acquainted with all parts of the continent on account of its great size, that the position of some parts on account of the carelessness of travelers was not correctly handed down to him, and that there are other parts which happen at different times to have undergone variations on account of the cataclysms or changes in consequence of which they are known to have been partly broken up. It has been necessary therefore, as he himself says he also had to do, to pay more attention to the information gathered in our own times. We have therefore arranged matters so that in the plane projection we have followed Ptolemy as regards the new lands and some other things, while on the globe, which accompanies the plane, we have followed the description of Amerigo that we subjoin.

APPENDIX

BEFORE closing, we shall add to the foregoing, as an appendix or corollary, a quadrant by which may be determined the elevation of the pole, the zenith, the center of the horizon, and the climates; although, if rightly considered, this quadrant, of which we shall speak, has a bearing on this subject. For a cosmographer ought to know especially the elevation of the pole, the zenith, and the climates of the earth. This quadrant, then, is constructed in the following way. Divide any circle into four parts in such a way that the two diameters intersect at the center at right angles. One of these, which has sights at either end, will represent the axis of the poles of the world, the other the equator. Then divide that part of the circle which is between the semi-axis that has the sights and the other semi-diameter into ninety parts and the opposite part also into the same number, fix a plumb-line to the center, and your quadrant will be ready. The quadrant is used as follows: turn it so that you will see the

pole directly through the openings in the sights
and then toward the climate and the degree to
which the plumb-line will fall. Your region, as
well as your zenith and the center of your horizon,
lies in that climate and at that degree of elevation.

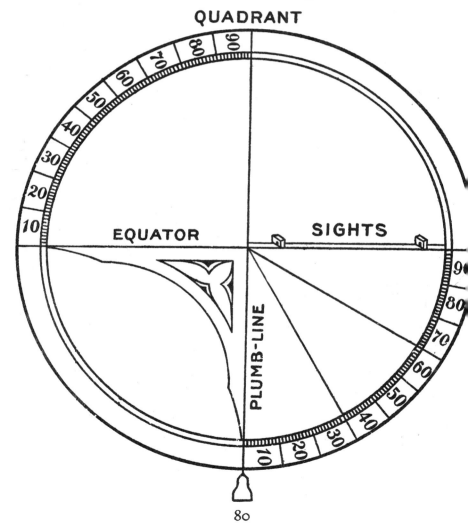

QUADRANT

Appendix

Having now finished the chapters that we proposed to take up, we shall here include the distant voyages of Vespucci, setting forth the consequences of the several facts as they bear upon our plan.

THE END OF THE OUTLINES

PHILESIUS, BORN IN THE VOSGES

To the Reader

Where the fields enriched by the papyrus-producing Siris flower and the lakes of the Moon give birth to mighty rivers, on the right are the mountains of Ius, Danchis, and Mascha, at the foot of which dwell the Ethiopians. From this region rises Africus (southwest wind), which with Libonotus (west-southwest wind) blows over the heated lands. From the other direction blows Vulturnus (east-southeast wind) upon a sweltering people, coming, as it does, in its rapid course over the Indian Ocean. There under the equator lies Taprobana, while Bassa is seen in the Prasodes Sea. Beyond Ethiopia and Bassa in the sea lies a land unknown to your maps, Ptolemy, situated under the tropic of Capricorn and its companion Aquarius. To the right lies a land encircled by the vast ocean and inhabited by a race of naked men. This land was discovered by him whom fair Lusitania boasts of as her king, and who sent a fleet across the sea. But why say more? The position and the customs of the newly-discovered race are set forth in Amerigo's book. Read this, honest reader, with all sincerity and do not imitate the rhinoceros.

THE END

THE FOUR VOYAGES OF AMERIGO VESPUCCI

TRANSLATED FROM THE FRENCH INTO LATIN

The Translator's Decastich to the Reader.

You who will read, perchance, this slender tome
Will find within a voyage deftly told.
It tells of lands and peoples lately found;
A novel tale well suited to amuse.
A worthy task for Maro's lofty pen,
Which dressed in noble words a theme sublime.
He who the Trojan heroes wand'ring sang
Should eke have sung thy voyages, Vespucci.
When in our book you've visited these lands,
The contents probe; 'tis not the writer's care.

Distich to the Reader.

Since what is new and well told pleases you,
I bring you what's amusing here and new.

THE END.

THE FOUR VOYAGES OF
AMERIGO VESPUCCI

To the most illustrious René, King of Jerusalem and of Sicily, Duke of Lorraine and Bar, Amerigo Vespucci pays humble homage and presents appropriate recommendations.

Perchance, most illustrious King, your majesty will be astonished at my foolhardiness, because I feel no apprehension in addressing to you the present long letter, even though I know you to be incessantly occupied with matters of the highest importance and with numerous affairs of State. And I shall be considered not only a presumptuous man but one who has accomplished a useless work in undertaking to send you also a story which hardly concerns your position, addressed by name to Ferdinand, King of Castile, and written in an unattractive and quite unpolished style, as if I were a man unacquainted with the Muses and a stranger to the refining influence of learning. My trust in your merits, and the absolute truth of the following accounts (on matters which neither ancient nor modern authors have written), will perhaps excuse me to your Majesty.

I was urged to write chiefly by the bearer of
the present letters, Benvenuto, an humble servant
of your Majesty and a friend of whom I need not
be ashamed. When this gentleman found me at
Lisbon, he begged me to acquaint your Majesty
with the things seen by me during my four
voyages to different quarters of the globe. For,
you must know that I have completed four
voyages of discovery to new lands: two of them
were undertaken by the order of Ferdinand, the
illustrious King of Castile, and carried me
toward the west, through the Great Gulf of the
Ocean; the other two were undertaken at the
command of Manuel, King of Portugal, and
carried me toward the south.

I have therefore prepared myself for the task
urged upon me by Benvenuto, hoping that your
Majesty will not exclude me from the number
of your insignificant servants, especially if you
recollect that formerly we were good friends. I
refer to the years of our youth, when we were
fellow-students, and together drank in the elements of grammar under the holy and vener-
able friar of St. Mark, my uncle, Friar
Giorgio Antonio Vespucci—a man of good life
and tried learning. Had it been possible for me
to follow in his footsteps, I should be quite a
different man to-day, as Petrarch says. However that may be, I am not ashamed of being

what I am ; for I have always taken pleasure in virtue for its own sake and in scholarship. If, then, these narratives give you no pleasure whatever, I shall repeat the words which Pliny once wrote to Mæcenas, "Formerly you were wont to take delight in my pleasantry." Your Majesty, it is true, is ever occupied with affairs of State ; still, you can secretly steal just a little time in which to read these accounts, trifling though they be. I assure you that their very novelty will please. You will find in these pages no slight relief from the wasting cares and problems of government. My book will serve you as the sweet fennel, which, when taken after meals, is wont to leave a pleasant breath and to promote a better digestion.

If, by chance, I have been more prolix than the subject warrants, I crave your indulgence.

Farewell.

PREFACE

MOST illustrious King! Your Majesty must know that I came to this country primarily as a merchant. I continued in that career for the space of four years. But when I observed the various changes of fortune, and saw how vain and fleeting riches are, and how for a time they lift man to the top of the wheel and then hurl him headlong to the bottom—him, who had boasted of wide possessions;—when I saw all this, and after I had personally suffered such experiences, I determined to abandon the business career and to devote all my efforts to worthier and more enduring ends.

And so I set about visiting different parts of the world and seeing its many wonders. Both time and place were favorable to my plans. For Ferdinand, King of Castile, was at that time fitting out four ships to discover new lands in the west, and His Highness made me one of that company of explorers. We set sail from the harbor of Cadiz on the 20th of May, 1497, making our way through the Great Gulf of the

Ocean. This voyage lasted eighteen months, during which we discovered many lands and almost countless islands (inhabited as a general rule), of which our forefathers make absolutely no mention. I conclude from this that the ancients had no knowledge of their existence. I may be mistaken; but I remember reading somewhere that they believed the sea to be free and uninhabited. Our poet Dante himself was of this opinion, when, in the 18th canto of the Inferno, he pictures the death of Ulysses. From the following pages, however, your Majesty will learn of the marvels I saw.

A description of the chief lands and of various islands, of which ancient authors make no mention, but which recently, in the 1497th year from the incarnation of Our Lord, were discovered in the course of four ocean voyages undertaken by order of their Serene Highnesses of Spain and Portugal. Of these voyages, two were through the western sea, by order of King Ferdinand of Castile; the remaining two were through southern waters, by order of Manuel, King of Portugal. To the above-mentioned Lord Ferdinand, King of Castile, Amerigo Vespucci, one of the foremost captains and commanders of that fleet, dedicates the following account of the new lands and islands.

THE FIRST VOYAGE

In the year of Our Lord 1497, on the 20th day of May, we set sail from the harbor of Cadiz in four ships. On our first run, with the wind blowing between the south and the southwest[1], we made the islands formerly called the Fortunate Islands, but now the Grand Canary, situated at the edge of the inhabited west and within the third climate. At this place, the North Pole rises 27⅔ degrees above the horizon, the islands themselves being 280 leagues from the city of Lisbon, in which this present pamphlet was written. There we spent almost eight days, providing ourselves with fuel and water and other necessary things. Then, after first offering our prayers to God, we raised and spread our sails to the wind, shaping our course to the west, with a point to southwest. We kept on this course for some time, and just as the 27th day was past we reached an unknown land, the mainland as we thought. It was distant from the islands of the Grand Canary 1000 leagues, more or less; it was inhabited, and was situated in the Torrid Zone. This we ascertained from the following observations: that the North Pole rises 16 degrees above the horizon of this new land, and that it is 75 degrees more to the west

[1]Vespucci names the wind according to the point toward which it blows.

than the islands of Grand Canary—at least so all
our instruments showed.

Here we dropped the bow anchors and stationed our fleet a league and a half from the
shore. We then lowered a few boats, and, filling them with armed men, we pulled as far as
the land. The moment we approached, we rejoiced not a little to see hordes of naked people
running along the shore. Indeed, all those whom
we saw going about naked seemed also to be
exceedingly astonished at us, I suppose because
they noticed that we wore clothing, and presented a different appearance from them. When
they realized that we had actually arrived, they
all fled to a hill near by; and though we beck-
oned to them and made signs of peace and friendship, we could not induce them to approach.
When night closed rapidly upon us, we felt some
fear in trusting our ships in such a dangerous
roadstead, for there was here no protection against
violent seas. We therefore agreed to depart
early the next morning in search of some harbor
where we might station our ships in a safe
anchorage. After we had formed this resolu-
tion, we spread our sails to a gentle breeze blowing along the shore, keeping land always in sight
and continually seeing the inhabitants along the
beach. In this way we sailed for two whole
days, and discovered a place quite suited to our

ships, where we anchored only one-half a league from the land. Here we again saw countless hordes of people. Desiring to see them close by and to speak with them, on that very day we approached the shore in our boats and skiffs, and then we landed in good order, about forty strong. The natives, however, showed themselves very loath to approach us or have anything to do with us. We could do nothing to induce them to speak with us or to enter upon any kind of communication. But finally, by dint of much labor undertaken with this one purpose in view, we managed to allure a few of them by giving them little bells and mirrors and pieces of crystal and other such trifles. In this way they became quite easy about us. They now came to meet us, and in fact to treat concerning terms of peace and friendship. At nightfall we took leave of them and returned to our ships. The next day, when the sun was quite risen, we again saw upon the beach an endless number of men and women, the latter carrying their children with them. We furthermore noticed that they were bringing with them all their household utensils, which will be described below in their proper place. The nearer we approached the shore, more and more of the natives jumped into the water (for there are many expert swimmers among them), and swam out the distance of a crossbow shot to meet us. They received us kindly, and in fact mingled among us with as complete assurance as if we had often met before and had frequently had dealings together. At this we were then very little pleased.

And now (so far as occasion permits), we shall devote some space to a description of their customs,—such as we were able to observe.

ON THE CUSTOMS OF THE NATIVES AND THEIR MODE OF LIFE

In regard to their life and customs, all of them, both men and women, go about entirely naked, with no more covering for their private parts than when they were born. The men are of medium size, but are very well proportioned. The color of their skin approaches red, like the hair of a lion, and I believe that, if it were their custom to wear clothing, they would be as fairskinned as we are. They have no hair on their body, with the exception of that on the head, which is long and black, particularly that of the women, who are beautiful for this very reason. Their features are not very handsome, because they have broad cheek-bones like the Tartars. They do not allow any hair to grow on their eyebrows nor their eyelids nor anywhere on their body (with the exception of the head), for this reason,—because they deem it coarse and animal-like to have hair on the body.

All of them, both men and women, are graceful in walking and swift in running. Indeed, even their women (as we have often witnessed) think nothing of running a league or two, wherein they greatly excel us Christians. They all swim remarkably well, in fact better than one would believe possible ; and the women are far better swimmers than the men, a statement which I can make with authority, for we frequently saw them swim in the sea for two leagues without any assistance whatsoever.

Their weapons are the bow and arrow, which they have learned to make very skillfully. They are unacquainted with iron and the metals, and consequently, in place of iron, they tip their arrows with the teeth of animals and fishes, and they also often harden the arrows by burning their ends. They are expert archers, with the result that they strike with their arrows whatever they aim at. In some places also the women are very skillful with the bow and arrow. They have other weapons also, such as spears or stakes sharpened at the ends, and clubs with wonderfully carved heads.

They are wont to wage war upon neighbors speaking a different language, fighting most mercilessly and sparing none, except to reserve them for more cruel torture later. When they go forth to battle, they take their wives with them, not that they too may participate in the fight, but that they may carry behind the fighting men all the necessary provisions. For, as we ourselves have often seen, any woman among them can place on her back, and then carry for thirty or forty leagues, a greater burden than a man (and even a strong man) can lift from the ground. They have no generals and no captains; in fact, since every one is his own leader, they go forth to war in no definite order. They never fight for power or territory, or for any other improper motive. Their one cause for war is an enmity of long standing, implanted in them from olden times. When questioned concerning the cause of such hostility, they give no other reason except that it is to avenge the death of their ancestors. Living as they do in perfect liberty, and obeying no man's word, they have neither king nor lord.

They are, however, especially inclined to war, and gird themselves for braver efforts when one of their own number is either a captive in the hands of the enemy or has been killed by them. In that case the oldest blood-relation of the prisoner or murdered man rises, rushes forth into the roads and villages, shouting and calling upon all, and urging them to hasten into battle with him to avenge the death of his kinsman. All are quickly stirred to the same feeling, gird themselves for the fight and make a sudden dash upon their enemies.

They observe no laws, and execute no justice. They do not punish their evildoers; indeed, not even the parents rebuke or chastise their children; and, wonderful to relate, we several times saw them quarrel among themselves. They are simple in their speech, but very shrewd and crafty. They speak rarely ; and when they do speak, it is in a low tone, using the same sounds as we. On the whole they shape their words either on the teeth or the lips, employing, of course, different words from those of our language. They have many different idioms, for we found such a variety of tongues in every hundred leagues that they do not understand one another.

They observe most barbarous customs in their eating ; indeed, they do not take their meals at any fixed hours, but eat whenever they are so inclined, whether it be day or night. At meals they recline on the ground, and do not use either tablecloths or napkins, being entirely unacquainted with linen and other kinds of cloth. The food is served in earthen pots which they make themselves, or else in receptacles made out of half-gourds. They sleep in a species of large net made of cotton and suspended in the air ; and though this mode of sleeping may appear odd and uncomfortable, I testify that, on the contrary, it is very pleasant ; for it was frequently my lot to sleep in such nets, and I had a feeling of greater comfort then than when under the coverlets which we had with us.

In their person they are neat and clean, for the reason that they bathe very frequently.

*   *   *   *   *

In their sexual intercourse they have no legal obligations. In fact, each man has as many wives as he covets, and he can repudiate them later whenever he pleases, without its being considered an injustice or disgrace, and the women enjoy the same rights as the men. The men are not very jealous ; they are, however, very sensual. The women are even more so than the men. I have deemed it best (in the name of decency) to pass over in silence their many arts to gratify their insatiable lust. They are very prolific in bearing children, and do not omit performing their usual labors and tasks during the period of pregnancy. They are delivered with very little pain,—so true is this that on the very next day they are completely recovered and move about everywhere with perfect ease. In fact, immediately after the delivery they go to some stream to wash, and then come out of the water as

whole and as clean as fishes. However, they
are of such a cruel nature and harbor such violent hatreds that, if the husbands chance to anger
them, they immediately commit some wrong.
For instance, to appease their great wrath, they
kill the fetus within their own wombs, and then
cause an abortion. In this way countless off-
spring are destroyed. They have handsome, well-
proportioned and well-knit figures; indeed, no
blemish can possibly be discovered in them. . . .

No one of this race, as far as we saw, observed any religious law. They can not justly be
called either Jews or Moors; nay, they are far
worse than the gentiles themselves or the pagans,
for we could not discover that they performed
any sacrifices nor that they had any special
places or houses of worship. Since their life is
so entirely given over to pleasure, I should style
it Epicurean.

They hold their habitations in common.
Their dwellings are bell-shaped, and are strongly
built of large trees fastened together, and covered
with palm leaves, which offer ample protection
against the winds and storms. In some places
these dwellings were so large that we found as
many as six hundred persons living in a single
building. Of all these dwellings we found that
eight were most thickly populated; in fact, that
ten thousand souls lived within them at one and

the same time. Every eight or seven years they move the seat of their abodes. When asked the reason for this, they gave a most natural answer. They said that it was on account of the continual heat of a strong sun, and because, from dwelling too long in the same place, the air became infected and contaminated, and brought about various diseases of the body. And in truth, their point seemed to us to be well taken.

Their riches consist of variegated birds' feathers, and of strings of beads (like our *pater nosters*), made of fish bones, or of green or white stones. These they wear as ornaments on the forehead, or suspended from their lips and ears. Many other such useless trifles are considered riches by them, things to which we attach no value whatever. Among them there is neither buying nor selling, nor is there an exchange of commodities, for they are quite content with what nature freely offers them. They do not value gold, nor pearls, nor gems, nor such other things as we consider precious here in Europe. In fact they almost despise them, and take no pains to acquire them. In giving, they are by nature so very generous that they never deny anything that is asked of them. But as soon as they have admitted any one to their friendship, they are just as eager to ask and to receive. The greatest and surest seal of their friendship is this : that they place at the disposal of their friends their own wives and daughters, both parents considering themselves highly honored if any one deigns to lead their daughter (even though yet a maiden) into concubinage. In this way (as I have said) they seal the bond of their friendship.

In burying the dead they follow many different customs. Some, indeed, follow the practice of inhumation, placing at the head water and food, for they believe that the dead will eat and subsist thereupon. But there is no further grief at their departure, and they perform no other ceremonies. In some places a most barbarous and inhuman rite is practised. When any one of their fellow-tribesmen is believed to be at the point of death, his relations take him into some great forest, where they place him in one of those nets in which they are accustomed to sleep. They then suspend him thus reclining between two trees, dance around him for a whole day, and then at nightfall return to their habitations, leaving at the head of the dying man water and food to last him about four days. If at the end of this period the sick man can eat and drink, becomes convalescent, regains his health, and returns to his own habitation, then all his relations, whether by blood or marriage, welcome him with the greatest ceremonies. But there are few who can pass safely through so severe an ordeal. Indeed, no one ever visits the sick man after he is abandoned in the woods. Should he, therefore, chance to die, he receives no further burial. They have many other savage rites of burial, which I shall not mention, to avoid the charge of being too prolix.

In their sicknesses they employ many different kinds of medicines, so different from ours and so discordant with our ideas that we wondered not a little how any one could possibly survive. For, as we learned from frequent experience, if any one of them is sick with fever, they immerse and bathe him in very cold water just when the fever is at its height. Then they compel him to run back and forth for two hours around a very warm fire until he is fairly aglow with heat, and finally lead him off to sleep. We saw very many of them restored to health by this treatment. Very frequently they practise also dieting as one of their cures, for they can do without food and drink for three or four days. Again, they commonly draw blood, not from their arms (with the exception of the shoulder-blade), but from their loins and the calves of their legs. Often they bring about vomiting by chewing certain herbs which they use as medicines; and they have, in addition, many other cures and remedies which it would be tedious to enumerate.

They are full-blooded and phlegmatic, owing to the food they eat, which consists chiefly of roots, fruits, herbs, and fishes of different kinds. They do not raise crops of spelt or of any other grain. Their most common food is a certain root which they grind into a fairly good flour and which some of the natives call *iucha*, others *chambi*, and still others *ygnami*.[1] They very rarely eat flesh, with the exception of human flesh ; and in this they are so inhuman and so savage as to outdo even the wild animals. Indeed, all the enemies whom they either kill or capture, without discriminating between the men and the women, are relished by them with such savageness that nothing more barbarous and cruel can either be seen or heard of. Time and again it fell to my lot to see them engaged in this savage and brutal practice, while they expressed their wonder that we did not likewise eat our enemies. Your royal Majesty may rest assured on this point, that their numerous customs are all so barbarous that I can not describe them adequately here. Therefore, considering the many, many things I saw in my four voyages—things so entirely different from our customs and manners—I have prepared and com-

[1] The Italian text gives *iuca*, *cazabi*, and *ignami*.

pleted a work which I have entitled "The Four Voyages." In this book I have collected the greater part of the things I saw, and have described them as clearly as my small ability would permit. I have not, however, published it as yet. In this work, each topic is given more careful and individual attention, and therefore in the present pamphlet I shall merely touch upon them, making only general statements. And so I return to complete the account of our first voyage, from which I have made a short digression.

In the beginning of our voyage we did not see anything of great value except a few traces of gold, and this only because they pointed out to us several proofs of its existence in the soil. I suppose we should have learned much more, had we been able to understand their language. In truth, this land is so happily situated that it could not be improved. We unanimously agreed, however, to leave it and to continue our voyage further. And so, keeping land always in sight, and tacking frequently, we visited many ports, in the meanwhile entering upon communications with many different tribes of those regions. After some days we made a certain harbor in which it pleased God to deliver us from a great danger.

As soon as we entered this harbor, we discovered that their whole population, that is to say, the entire village, had houses built in the water, as at Venice. There were in all about twenty large houses, built in the shape of bells (as we have said above), and resting firmly upon strong wooden piles. In front of the doors of each house drawbridges had been erected, over which one could pass from one hut to another as if over a well-constructed road. As soon as the inhabitants of this settlement noticed us they were seized with great fear, and immediately raised the drawbridges to defend themselves against us, and hid themselves within their houses. While we were watching their actions with some degree of wonder, lo and behold about twelve of their boats (which are hollowed out of the trunk of a single tree) came over the water to meet us. The occupants of these boats looked at us and at our clothes with wonder, and rowed about us in every direction, but continued to examine us from a distance. We on our part were similarly observing them, making many signs of friendship to urge them to approach us without fear. But it was of no avail. Seeing their reluctance, we began to row in their direction. They did not await our arrival, but immediately fled to the shore, making signs to us that we should await their return, which (they signified) would be shortly. There-

upon they hurried to a nearby hill, returning
thence accompanied by sixteen maidens. With
these they embarked in the above-mentioned
boats and straightway returned to us. Of the
maidens, four were then placed in each one of
our ships, a proceeding which, as your Majesty
may well believe, astonished us not a little.
Then they went back and forth among our ships
with their canoes, and spoke to us in such
kindly manner that we began to consider them
our trusty friends. While all this was going on,
behold a large crowd began to swim from their
houses (already described) and to advance in our
direction. Though they advanced further and
further, and though they were now nearing our
ships, we entertained not the slightest suspicion
of their actions. At this point, however, we saw
some old women standing at the doors of their
houses, shouting wildly and filling the air with
their cries, and tearing their hair in great distress.
We now began to suspect that some great
danger was threatening. Immediately the girls
who had been placed on board our ships leaped
into the sea. Those who were in the canoes
pulled off a short distance, drew their bows and
began to make a vigorous attack upon us. Moreover, those who had started from their houses
and were swimming over the sea toward us,
were, each one of them, carrying a lance under

water. This was sure proof of their treachery, and we began not only to defend ourselves with spirit, but also to inflict serious injuries upon them. In fact, we wrecked and sank many of the canoes, with great loss of life to their occupants,—a loss which became even greater because the natives abandoned their canoes entirely and swam to the shore. About twenty of them were killed and many more were wounded. Of ours only five were injured, all of whom were restored to health, with the help of God. We managed to capture two of the girls and three men. Later we visited the houses of the settlement, and upon entering found them occupied only by two old women and a sick man. We did not set fire to the houses for this reason, that we feared lest our consciences would prick us. We then returned to the ships with our five captives and put them in irons, except the girls. At night, however, both girls and one of the men very shrewdly effected their escape.

On the following day we agreed to leave that port and to sail on along the coast. After a run of about eighty leagues we came to another tribe entirely different from the former in language and customs. We anchored the fleet and approached the shore in our small boats. Here we saw a crowd of about 4,000 persons on the beach. As soon as they realized that we were

about to land, they no longer remained where
they were, but fled to the woods and forests,
abandoning on the shore everything which they
had had with them. Leaping upon the land,
we advanced along a road leading to the forest
about as far as a crossbow shot. We soon came
upon many tents which had been pitched there
by that tribe for the fishing season. Within
them, many fires had been built for cooking
their meals, and animals and fishes of various
kinds were being roasted. Among other things
we saw that a certain animal was being roasted
which looked very much like a serpent, except
for the wings which were missing. It looked
so strange and so terrible that we greatly wondered at its wild appearance. Proceeding onward
through their tents, we found many similar serpents, whose feet were tied and whose mouths
were muzzled so that they could not open them,
as is done with dogs and other wild animals that
they may not bite. Their whole appearance
was so savage that we, supposing them to be
poisonous, did not dare approach them. They
are like a young goat in size, and half as long
again as an arm. Their feet are very large and
heavy, and are armed with strong claws; their
skin is varicolored; their mouth and face like
those of a serpent. From the end of the nose
to the tip of their tail they are covered (along

the back) with a kind of bristle, from which we decided that they were truly serpents. And yet the above-mentioned tribe eats them. That same tribe makes bread from the fishes which they catch in the sea, the process being as follows: First of all they place the fish in water and boil it for some time; then they pound it and crush it and make it into small cakes which they bake upon hot ashes and which they then eat. Upon tasting them we found them to be not at all bad. They have many other kinds of food, including different fruits and herbs, but it would take too long to describe them.

But to return to our story. Although the natives did not reappear from the woods to which they had fled, we did not take away any of their possessions, in order that we might increase their confidence in us. In fact, we left many small trifles in their tents, placing them where they would be seen, and at night returned to our ships. On the next day, when Titan began to rise above the horizon, we saw a countless multitude upon the shore. We immediately landed; and though the natives still appeared to be somewhat afraid of us, yet they mingled among us, and began to deal and to converse with us with complete security. They signified to us that they would be our friends, that the tents which we saw were not their real houses, and that they had come to the shore to fish. Therefore they begged us to accompany them to their villages, assuring us that they wished to welcome us as friends. We were made to understand that the cause of the friendship which they had conceived for us was our arrest of those two prisoners, who turned out to be enemies of theirs. And so, seeing the persistence with which they asked us, twenty-three of us decided to go with them, fully armed and with the firm resolve to die valiantly if need be.

After remaining there for three days, we marched inland with them for three leagues and came to a village consisting of but nine habitations. There we were received with such numerous and such barbarous ceremonies that my pen is too weak to describe them. For instance, we were welcomed with dances and with songs, with lamentations mingled with cries of joy and of happiness, with much feasting and banqueting. Here we rested for the night, and the natives most generously offered us their wives. . . . After we had remained that night and half of the next day, a large and wondering crowd came to look at us, without hesitation and fear. Their elders now asked us to go with them to their other villages situated farther inland, to which we again agreed. It is not an easy task to recount the honors which they

showered upon us here. In short, we went
about in their company for nine whole days,
visiting very many of their settlements, with the
result that (as we afterward learned), our companions whom we had left in the ships began to
be very anxious about us and to entertain
serious fears for our safety. And so, after having penetrated about eighteen leagues into the
interior of the country, we decided to make our
way back to the ships. On our return a great
crowd of men and women met us and accompanied us all the way to the sea,—a fact which
is of itself very remarkable. But there is more.
Whenever it happened that one of our company
would lag behind from weariness, the natives
came to his assistance and carried him most
zealously in those nets in which they sleep. In
crossing the rivers, too (which in their country
are very numerous and very large), they were so
careful with the contrivances they employed
that we never feared the slightest danger. Moreover, many of them, laden down with their
gifts, which they carried in those same nets, accompanied us. The gifts consisted of feathers
of very great value, of many bows and arrows,
and of numberless parrots of different colors.
Many others, also, were bringing their household goods and their animals. In fine, they all
reckoned themselves fortunate if, in crossing a

stream, they could bear us on their shoulders or on their backs.

However, we hastened to the sea as quickly as possible. As we were about to embark in our boats, so great was the crowding of the natives in their attempt to accompany us still further and to embark with us and visit our ships, that our boats were almost swamped by the load. We took on board, however, as many as we could accommodate and brought them to our ships. In addition to those whom we had on board, so many of them accompanied us by swimming that we were somewhat troubled by their approach ; for, about a thousand of them boarded our ships (naked and unarmed though they were), and examined with wonder our equipment and arrangements and the great size of the ships themselves. And then a laughable thing happened. We desired to shoot off some of our war engines and artillery, and therefore put a match to the guns. These went off with such a loud report that a large portion of the natives, upon hearing this new thunder, leaped into the water and swam away, like frogs sitting on the bank, which jump into the bottom of the marsh and hide the moment they are startled by a noise. In this way acted the natives. Those natives who had fled to another portion of the ships were so thoroughly frightened that we repented and chid ourselves for what we had done. But we quickly reassured them, and did not permit them to remain any longer in ignorance, explaining that it was with these guns that we killed our enemies.

After entertaining them the whole day upon our ships, we warned them to depart because we intended to sail during the night; whereupon they took leave of us in a most friendly and kindly manner. We saw and learned very many customs of this tribe and region, but it is not my intention to dwell upon them here. Your Majesty will be in a position to learn later of all the more wonderful and noteworthy things I saw in each of my voyages; for I have collected them in one work written after the manner of a geographical treatise and entitled "The Four Voyages." In this work I give individual and detailed descriptions, but I have not yet offered it to the public because I must still revise it and verify my statements.

That land is very thickly populated, and everywhere filled with many different animals, very unlike those of our country. In common with us they have lions, bears, stags, pigs, goats, and fallow deer, which are, however, distinguished from ours by certain differences. They are entirely unacquainted with horses, mules, asses, dogs, and all kinds of small cattle (such as sheep and the like), and cows and oxen. They have, however, many species of animals which it would be difficult to name, all of them wild and of no use to them in their domestic affairs. But why say more? The land is very rich in birds, which are so numerous and so large, and have plumes of such different kinds and colors, that to see and describe them fills us with wonder. The climate, moreover, is very temperate and the land fertile, full of immense forests and groves, which are always green, for the leaves never fall. The fruits are countless and entirely different from ours. The land itself is situated in the torrid zone, on the edge of the second climate, precisely on the parallel which marks the tropic of Cancer, where the Pole rises twenty-three degrees above the horizon. During this voyage many came to look at us, marveling at the whiteness of our skin. And when they asked us whence we came, we answered that we had descended from heaven to pay the earth a visit, a statement which was believed on all sides. We established in this land many baptismal fonts or baptisteries, in which they made us baptize countless numbers, calling us in their own tongue " charaibi,"—that is to say, "men of great wisdom." The country itself is called by them " Parias."

Later we left that harbor and land, sailing

along shore and keeping land always in view.
We sailed for 870 leagues, making many tacks
and treating and dealing with numerous tribes.
In many places we obtained gold, but not in
great quantities ; for it sufficed us for the present
to discover those lands and to know that there
was gold therein. And since by that time we
had already been thirteen months on our voyage,
and since the tackle and rigging were very
much the worse for wear and the men were re-
duced by fatigue, we unanimously agreed to
repair our small boats (which were leaking at
every point) and to return to Spain. Just as we
had reached this conclusion, we neared and
entered the finest harbor in the world. Here
we again met a countless multitude, who received us in a very friendly manner. On the
beach we built a new boat with material taken
from the other ships and from barrels and casks,
placed upon dry land our rigging and military
engines, which were almost rotting away in the
water, lightened our ships and drew them up on
land. Then we repaired them and patched
them, and gave them a- thorough overhauling.
During all these occupations the inhabitants of
the country gave us no slight assistance. Indeed,
they offered us provisions out of friendship and
unasked, so that we consumed very little of our
own supplies. This we considered a great boon,

for our supplies at this stage were rather too meager to enable us to reach Spain without stinting ourselves.

We remained in that port thirty-seven days, frequently visiting the villages in company with the natives and being treated with great respect by each and every one of them. When we at last expressed our intention to leave that harbor and to resume our voyage, the natives complained to us that there was a certain savage and hostile tribe, which, at a certain time of the year, came over the sea to their land, and either through treachery or through violence killed and devoured a great number of them. They added that others were led off as prisoners to the enemy's country and home, and that they could not defend themselves against these enemies, making us understand that that tribe inhabited an island about one hundred leagues out at sea. They related their story to us in such plaintive tones that we took pity on them and believed them, promising that we should exact punishment for the injuries inflicted upon them. Whereat they greatly rejoiced and of their own accord offered to accompany us. We refused for several reasons, agreeing to take seven with us on the following condition: that at the close of the expedition they should return to their country alone and in their own canoes,

for we did not by any means intend to take the
trouble of bringing them back. To this condition they gladly assented, and so we took
leave of the natives, who had become our dear
friends, and departed.

We sailed about in our refitted ships for seven
days, with the wind blowing between the northeast and east. At the end of this period we
reached many islands, of which some were inhabited and others not. We thereupon approached one of them; and while endeavoring
to anchor our ships we saw a great horde of
people on the island, which the inhabitants call
Ity. After examining them for some time, we
manned the small boats with brave men and
three guns, and rowed nearer the shore, which
was filled with 400 men and very many women,
all of whom (like the others) went about naked.
The men were well built, and seemed very warlike and brave, for they were all equipped with
their usual arms, namely, the bow and arrow
and the lance. Very many of them, moreover,
bore round shields or even square shields, with
which they defended themselves so skillfully
that they were not hindered thereby in shooting
their arrows.

When we had come in our boats to within a
bowshot of the land, they leaped into the sea
and shot an infinite number of arrows at us,

endeavoring might and main to prevent our landing. Their bodies were all painted over with many colors, and were decorated with birds' feathers. The natives whom we had taken with us noticed this and informed us that whenever the men are so painted and adorned with plumes they are ready for battle. They were, however, so successful in preventing our landing that we were compelled to direct our stone-hurling machines against them. When they heard the report and noticed its power (for many of them had fallen dead), they fled to the shore. We then held a consultation, and forty-two of us agreed to land after them and valiantly to engage in battle with them. This we did. We leaped to the shore fully armed; and the natives made such stout resistance that the battle raged ceaselessly for almost two hours with varying fortune. We gained a signal victory over them, but only a very few of the natives were killed, and not by us but by our cross-bowmen and gunners, which was due to the fact that they very shrewdly avoided our spears and swords. But at last we made a rush upon them with such vigor that we killed many with the points of our swords. When they saw this, and when very many had been killed and wounded, they turned in flight to the woods and forests, leaving us masters of the field. We did not wish to pursue them any further that day because we were too fatigued and preferred to make our way back to our ships. And the joy of the seven who had come with us from the mainland was so great that they could scarcely restrain themselves.

Early the next day we saw a great horde of people approaching through the island, playing on horns and other instruments which they use in war, and again painted and wearing birds' feathers. It was a wonderful sight to see. We again discussed what their plans might be, and decided upon the following course of action: to gather our forces quickly if the natives offered us any hostility; to keep constant watch in turns and in the meantime to endeavor to make them our friends, but to treat them as enemies if they rejected our friendship; and finally to capture as many of them as we could and make and keep them as our slaves forever. And so we gathered upon the shore in hollow formation, armed to the teeth. They, however, did not oppose the slightest resistance to our landing, I suppose on account of their fear of our guns. Upon disembarking, fifty-seven strong, we advanced against them in four divisions (each man under his respective captain), and engaged in a long hand-to-hand combat with them.

After a long and severe struggle, during which we inflicted great loss upon them, we put the rest to flight and pursued them as far as one of their settlements. Here we made twenty-five prisoners, set fire to the village, and returned to the ships with our captives. The losses of the enemy were very many killed and wounded; on our side, however, only one man was killed, and twenty-two were wounded, all of whom have regained their health, with the help of God.

Our arrangements for the return to our fatherland were now complete. To the seven natives who had come with us from the mainland (five of whom had been wounded in the aforesaid battle), we gave seven prisoners, three men and four women. And they, embarking in a boat which they had seized on the island, returned home filled with great joy and with great admiration for our strength. We set sail for Spain, and at last entered the harbor of Cadiz with our two hundred and twenty-two prisoners, on the 25th day of October, in the year of Our Lord 1499, where we were received with great rejoicing, and where we sold all our prisoners.

And these are what I have deemed to be the more noteworthy incidents of my first voyage.

THE SECOND VOYAGE

THE following pages contain an account of my second voyage and of the noteworthy incidents which befell me in the course of that voyage.

We set sail from the harbor of Cadiz, in the year of Our Lord 1489 (sic), on a May day · As soon as we cleared the harbor, we shaped our course for the Cape Verde Islands; and passing in sight of the islands of the Grand Canary group, we sailed on until we reached the island called Fire Island. Here we took on supplies of fuel and of water, and resumed our voyage with a southwest wind. After nineteen days we reached a new land, which we took to be the mainland. It was situated opposite to that land of which mention has been made in our first voyage; and it is within the Torrid Zone, south of the equinoctial line, where the pole rises five degrees above the horizon beyond every climate. The land is 500 leagues to the southwest of the above-mentioned islands.

We discovered that in this country the day is of the same length as the night on the 27th of · June, when the sun is on the Tropic of Cancer. Moreover, we found that the country is, in great measure, marshy and that it abounds in large rivers, which cause it to have very thick vegetation and very high and straight trees. In fact, the growth of vegetation was such that we could not at the time decide whether or not the country was inhabited. We stopped our ships and anchored them, and then lowered some of our small boats in which we made for the land. We hunted long for a landing, going here and there and back and forth, but, as has already been said, found the land everywhere so covered with water that there was not a single spot that was not submerged. We saw, however, along the banks of those rivers many indications that the land was not only inhabited, but indeed very thickly populated. We could not disembark to examine such signs of life more closely, and therefore agreed to return to our ships, which we did. We weighed anchor and sailed along the coast with the wind blowing east and southeast, trying time and again, in a course of more than forty leagues, to penetrate into the island itself. But all to no purpose. For we found in that part of the ocean so strong a current flowing from southeast to northwest that the sea was quite unfit for navigation. When we discovered this difficulty, we held a council and determined to turn back and head our ships to the northwest. So we continued to sail along shore and finally reached a body of water having an outer harbor and a most beautiful island at the entrance.

We sailed across the outer harbor that we might enter the inner haven. In so doing, we noticed a horde of natives on the aforesaid island, about four leagues inland from the sea. We were greatly pleased and got our boats ready to land. While we were thus engaged, we noticed a canoe coming in from the open sea with many persons on board, which made us resolve to attack them and make them our prisoners. We therefore began to sail in their direction and to surround them, lest they might escape us. The natives in their turn bent to their paddles and, as the breeze continued to blow but moderately, we saw them raise their oars straight on high, as if to say that they would remain firm and offer us resistance. I suppose that they did this in order to rouse admiration in us. But when they became aware that we were approaching nearer and nearer, they dipped their paddles into the water and made for the land. Among our ships there was a very swift boat of about forty-five tons, which was so headed that she soon got to windward of the natives. When the moment for attacking them had come, they got ready themselves and their gear and rowed off. Since our ship now went beyond the canoe of the natives, these attempted to effect their escape. Having lowered some boats and filled them with brave men, thinking that we would catch them, we soon bore down on them, but though we pursued them for two hours, had not our caravel which had passed them turned back on them they would have entirely escaped us. When they saw that they were hemmed in on all sides by our small boats and by the ship, all of them (about twenty in number) leaped into the water, albeit they were still about two leagues out at sea. We pursued them with our boats for that entire day, and yet we managed to capture only two of them, the rest reaching land in safety.

In the canoe which they had abandoned, there were four youths, who did not belong to the same tribe, but had been captured in another land. These youths had recently had their virile parts removed, a fact which caused us no little astonishment. When we had taken them on board our ships, they gave us to understand by signs that they had been carried off to be devoured, adding that this wild, cruel, and cannibal tribe were called "Cambali."

We then took the canoe in tow, and advanced with our ships to within half a league of the shore, where we halted and dropped our anchors. When we saw a very great throng of people roaming on the shore, we hastened to reach land in our small boats, taking with us the two men we had found in the canoe that we had attacked. The moment we set foot on dry land, they all fled in great fright to the groves near by and hid in their recesses. We then gave one of the captives permission to leave us, loading him with very many gifts for the natives with whom we desired to be friends, among which were little bells and plates of metal and numerous mirrors. We instructed him, furthermore, to tell the natives who had fled not to entertain any fear on our account, becau e we were greatly desirous of being their friends. Our messenger departed and fulfilled his mission so well that the entire tribe, about four hundred in number, came to us from out of the forest, accompanied by many women. Though unarmed, they came to where we were stationed with our small boats, and we became so friendly that we restored to them the second of the two men whom we had captured, and likewise sent instructions to our companions, in whose possession it was, to return to the natives the canoe which we had run down. This canoe was hollowed out of the trunk of a single tree, and had been fashioned with the greatest care. It was twenty-six paces long and two ells (bracchia) wide. As soon as the natives had recovered possession of their canoe and had placed it in a secure spot along the river bank, they unexpectedly fled from us and would no longer have anything to do with us. By such an uncivilized act, we knew them to be men of bad faith. Among them we saw a little gold, which they wore suspended from their ears.

We left that country, and after sailing about eighty leagues we found a safe anchorage for our ships, upon entering which we saw such numbers of natives that it was a wonderful sight. We immediately made friends with them and visited in their company many of their villages, where we were honorably and heartily welcomed. Indeed, we bought of them five hundred large pearls in return for one small bell, which we gave them for nothing.' In that land they drink wine made from fruits and seeds, which is like that made from chickpeas, or like white or red beer. The better kind of wine, however, is made from the choicest fruits of the myrrh tree. We ate heartily of these fruits and of many others that were both pleasant to the taste and nourishing, for we had arrived at the proper season. This island greatly abounds in what they use for food and utensils, and the people themselves were well mannered and more peacefully inclined than any other tribe we met.

We spent seventeen days in this harbor very pleasantly, and each day a great number of

'So the Latin text, which seems to be in error. The Italian version having, "which they gave us for nothing."

people would come to us to marvel at our appearance, the whiteness of our skins, our clothes and weapons, and at the great size of our ships. Indeed, they even told us that one of the tribes hostile to them lived further to the west, and possessed an infinite number of pearls; and that those pearls which they themselves possessed had been taken from these enemies in the course of wars which they had waged against them. They gave us further information as to how the pearls were fished and how they grew, all of which we found to be true, as your Majesty will learn later on.

We left that harbor and sailed along the coast, on which we always saw many people. Continuing on our course, we entered a harbor for the purpose of repairing one of our ships. Here again we saw many natives, whom we could neither force nor coax to communicate with us in any way. For, if we made any attempt to land, they resisted most desperately; and if they could not withstand our attack, they fled to the woods, never waiting for us to approach any nearer. Realizing their utter savageness, we departed. While we were thus sailing on, we saw an island fifteen leagues out at sea and resolved to visit it and learn whether or not it was inhabited. Upon reaching it we found it to be inhabited by a race of most animallike simplicity, and at the same time very obliging and kind, whose rites and customs are the following:

ON THE RITES AND CUSTOMS OF THIS TRIBE.

They were animallike in their appearance and actions, and had their mouths full of a certain green herb which they continually chewed upon as animals chew their cud, with the result that they could not speak. Moreover, each one of them had suspended from his neck two small dried gourds, one of which contained a supply of that herb which they were chewing, while the other contained a kind of white flour resembling plaster or white lime. Every now and then they would thrust into the gourd filled with flour a small stick whose end they had moistened in their mouths. By so doing they managed to gather some of the flour and put it into their mouths, powdering with this flour that herb which they were already chewing. They repeated this process at short intervals; and though we wondered greatly, we could not see any reason for their so doing, nor could we understand their secret.

This tribe came to us and treated us as familiarly as if they had frequently had dealings with us and as if they had long been friendly with us. We strolled with them along the shore, talking the while, and expressed our desire to drink some fresh water. To which they answered, by signs, that there was none in their country, offering us in its stead some herb and flour such as they were chewing. We now understood that since their country lacked water, they chewed that herb and flour to quench their thirst. And so it happened that, though we walked along that shore in their company for a day and a half, we never came across any spring water, and learned that such water as they did drink was the dew which gathered upon certain leaves having the shape of a donkey's ears. During the night these leaves were filled with dew, of which the people then drank, and it is very good. But in many places these leaves are not found.

This tribe is entirely unacquainted with the solid products of the earth, and live chiefly on the fish which they catch in the sea. Indeed there are many expert fishermen among them, and their waters abound in fish, of which they offered us many turtles and many other most excellent varieties. The women of the tribe, however, do not chew the herb as the men do ; in its place, each one of them carries a single gourd filled with water, of which they partake from time to time. They do not have villages composed of individual houses, nor do they have even small huts. Their only shelter is made of large leaves, which serve indeed to protect them against the heat of the sun, but are not a sufficient protection against the rains, from which it may be deduced that there is little rain in that country. When they come down to the sea to fish, each one brings with him a leaf so large that, by fixing one end of it in the ground and then turning the leaf to follow the sun, he procures underneath its shade ample relief from the great heat. In this island, finally, there are countless species of animals, all of which drink the water of the marshes.

Seeing, however, that there was nothing to be gained on that island, we left it and found another one. We landed and started to search for some fresh water to drink, believing the island to be uninhabited because we had seen no one as we approached it. But as we were walking along the shore, we came upon some very large footprints, from which we judged that, if the other members of the body were in proportion to the size of the feet, the inhabitants must be very large indeed. Continuing our walk along the sands, we discovered a road leading inland, along which nine of us decided to go to explore the island, because it did not seem to be very large nor very thickly populated. After advancing along that road about a league, we saw five houses situated in a valley

and apparently inhabited. Entering them we
found five women, two of them old and three
young; and all of them were of such large and
noble stature that we were greatly astonished.
As soon as they laid eyes upon us they were so
overcome with surprise that they had no strength
left for flight. Thereupon the old woman addressed us soothingly in their own tongue, and,
gathering in one hut, offered us great quantities
of food. All of them, in truth, were taller than
a very tall man; indeed, they were as tall as
Francesco degli Albizi, and better knit and
better proportioned than we are. When we had
observed all this, we agreed to seize the young
girls by force and to bring them to Castile as
objects of wonder.

While we were still deliberating, behold
about thirty-six men began to file through the
door of the house, men much larger than the
women and so magnificently built that it was a
joy to see them. These men caused us such
great uneasiness that we considered it safer to
return to our ships than to remain in their company. For they were armed with immense
bows and arrows, and with stakes and staffs the
size of long poles. As soon as they had all entered, they began to talk among themselves as
if plotting to take us prisoners, upon seeing
which we, too, held a consultation. Some were

of the opinion that we should fall upon them just where they were, within the hut itself; others disapproved of this entirely, and suggested that the attack be made out of doors and in the open; and still others declared that we should not force an engagement until we learned what the natives decided to do. During the discussion of these plans we left the hut disguising our feelings and our intentions, and began to make our way back to the ships. The natives followed at a stone's throw, always talking among themselves. I believe, however, that their fear was no less than ours; for, although they kept us in sight, they remained at a distance, not advancing a single step unless we did likewise. When, however, we had reached the ships and had boarded them in good order, the natives immediately leaped into the sea and shot very many of their arrows after us. But now we had not the slightest fear of them. Indeed, rather to frighten than to kill them, we shot two of our guns at them; and upon hearing the report they hastily fled to a hill nearby. Thus it was that we escaped from them and departed. These natives, like the others, also go about naked; and we called the island the Island of the Giants, on account of the great size of its inhabitants.

We continued our voyage further, sailing a

little further off shore than before and being
compelled to engage with the enemy every now
and then because they did not want us to take
anything out of their country. By this time
thoughts of revisiting Castile began to enter our
minds, particularly for this reason, that we had
now been almost a year at sea and that we had
very small quantities of provisions and other
necessaries left. Even what still remained was
all spoiled and damaged by the extreme heat
which we had suffered. For, ever since our departure from the Cape Verde Islands, we had
continually sailed in the Torrid Zone, and had
twice crossed the equator, as we have said above.

While we were in this state of mind, it pleased
the Holy Spirit to relieve us of our labors. For,
as we were searching for a suitable haven wherein to repair our ships, we reached a tribe which
received us with the greatest demonstrations of
friendship. We learned, moreover, that they
were the possessors of countless large Oriental
pearls. We therefore remained among them
forty-seven days, and bought 119 marcs of
pearls at a price which, according to our esti-
mation, was not greater than forty ducats, for we
gave them in payment little bells, mirrors, bits
of crystals, and very thin plates of electrum.
Indeed, each one would give all the pearls he
had for one little bell. We also learned from

them how and where the pearls were fished, and they gave us several of the shells in which they grow. We bought some shells in addition, finding as many as 130 pearls in some, and in others not quite so many. Your Majesty must know that unless the pearls grow to full maturity and of their own accord fall from the shells in which they are born, they cannot be quite perfect. Otherwise, as I have myself found by experience time and again, they soon dry up and leave no trace. When, however, they have grown to full maturity, they drop from the fleshy part into the shell, except the part by which it hung attached to the flesh; and these are the best pearls.

At the end of the forty-seven days, then, we took leave of that tribe with which we had become such good friends, and set sail for home on account of our lack of provisions. We · reached the island of Antiglia, which Christopher Columbus had discovered a few years before. Here we remained two months and two days in straightening out our affairs and repairing our ships. During this time we endured many annoyances from the Christians settled on that island, all of which I shall here pass over in silence that I may not be too prolix. We left that island on the 27th of July, and after a voyage of a month and a half we at last entered the harbor of Cadiz on the 8th of September, where we were received with great honor.

And so ended my second voyage, according to the will of God.

THE THIRD VOYAGE

I HAD taken up my abode in Seville, desiring to rest myself a little, to recover from the toils and hardships endured in the voyages described above, intending finally to revisit the land of pearls. But Fortune was by no means done with me. For some reason unknown to me she caused his most serene Lordship, Manuel, King of Portugal, to send me a special messenger bearing a letter which urgently begged me to go to Lisbon as soon as possible, because he had some important facts to communicate to me. I did not even consider the proposition, but immediately sent word by the same messenger that I was not feeling very well and in fact was ill at that moment; adding that, if I should regain my health and if it should still please His Royal Majesty to enlist my services, I should gladly undertake whatever he wished. Whereupon the King, who saw that he could not bring me to him just then, sent to me a second time, commissioning Giuliano Bartolomeo Giocondo¹,

¹ Probably a relative of Fra Giovanni, a Dominican, later Franciscan friar, architect, and archæologist, associated with Raphael and Sangallo in the erection of St. Peter's, builder of a bridge across the Seine and collector of more than 2,000 ancient inscriptions (1430?-1515?).

then in Lisbon, to leave no stone unturned to bring me back to the King. Upon the arrival of the said Giuliano I was moved by his entreaties to return with him to the King—a decision which was disapproved of by all those who knew me. For I was leaving Castile, where no small degree of honor had been shown me and where the King himself held me in high esteem. What was even worse was that I departed without taking leave of my host. I soon presented myself before King Manuel, who seemed to rejoice greatly at my arrival. He then repeatedly asked me to set out with three ships which had been got ready to start in search of new lands. And so, inasmuch as the entreaties of Kings are as commands, I yielded to his wishes.

THE START OF THE THIRD VOYAGE

WE set sail in three ships from the harbor of Lisbon, on the 10th of May, 1501, directing our course toward the islands of the Grand Canary. We sailed along in sight of these islands without stopping, and continued our westward voyage along the coast of Africa. We delayed three days in these waters, catching a great number of species of fish called *Parghi*. Proceeding thence we reached that region of Ethiopia which is called Besilicca', situated in

'Now Goree.

the Torrid Zone, within the first climate, and at a spot where the North Pole rises fourteen degrees above the horizon. We remained here eleven days to take on supplies of wood and of water, because it was my intention to sail southward through the Atlantic Ocean. We left that harbor of Ethiopia and sailed to the southwest for sixty-seven days, when we reached an island 700 leagues to the southwest of the above-mentioned harbor. During these days we encountered worse weather than any human being had ever before experienced at sea. There were high winds and violent rainstorms which caused us countless hardships. The reason for such inclement weather was that our ships kept sailing along the equinoctial line, where it is winter in the month of June and the days are as long as the nights, and where our own shadows pointed always to the south.

At last it pleased God to show us new land on the 17th of August. We anchored one league and a half out at sea, and then, embarking in some small boats, we set out to see whether or not the land was inhabited. We found that it was thickly inhabited by men who were worse than animals, as Your Royal Majesty will learn forthwith. Upon landing we did not see any of the natives, although from many signs which we noticed we concluded that the country must have many inhabitants. We took possession of the coast in the name of the most serene King of Castile, and found it to be a pleasant and fruitful and lovely land. It is five degrees south of the Equator. The same day we returned to our ships; and since we were suffering from the lack of fuel and water, we agreed to land again the following day and provide ourselves with what was necessary. Upon landing we saw on the topmost ridge of a hill many people who did not venture to descend. They were all naked and similar in both appearance and color to those we had met in the former voyages. Though we did our best to make them come down to us and speak with us, we could not inspire them with sufficient confidence. Seeing their obstinacy and waywardness, we returned to our ships at night, leaving on the shore (as they looked on) several small bells and mirrors and other such trifles.

When they saw that we were far out at sea, they came down from the mountain to take the things we had left them, and showed great wonder thereat. On that day we took on a supply of water only. Early in the morning of the next day, as we looked out from our ships, we saw a larger number of natives than before, building here and there along the shore fires which made a great deal of smoke. Supposing that they were thus inviting us, we rowed to the land. We now saw that a great horde of natives had collected, who, however, kept far away from us, making many signs that we should go with them into the interior. Wherefore two of our Christians declared themselves ready to risk their lives in this undertaking and to visit the natives in order to see for themselves what kind of people they were and whether they possessed any riches or aromatic spices. They begged the commander of the fleet so earnestly that he gave his consent to their departure. The two then prepared themselves for the expedition, taking along many trifles, for barter with the natives, and left us, with the understanding that they should make sure to return after five days at the most, as we should wait for them no longer.

They accordingly began their journey inland, and we returned to our ships, where we waited for eight whole days. On almost each of these days a new crowd would come to the shore, but never did they show a desire to enter into conversation with us. On the seventh day, while we again were making our way to the shore, we discovered that the natives had brought all their wives with them. As soon as we landed they sent many of their women to talk with us. But even the women did not trust us sufficiently. While we were waiting for them to approach, we decided to send to them one of our young men who was very strong and agile; and then, that the women might be the less fearful, the rest of us embarked in our small boats. The young man advanced and mingled among the women; they all stood around him, and touched and stroked him, wondering greatly at him. At this point a woman came down from the hill carrying a big club. When she reached the place where the young man was standing, she struck him such a heavy blow from behind that he immediately fell to the ground dead. The rest of the women at once seized him and dragged him by the feet up the mountain, whereupon the men who were on the mountain ran down to the shore armed with bows and arrows and began to shoot at us. Our men, unable to escape quickly because the boats scraped the bottom as they rowed, were seized with such terror that no one had any thought at the moment of taking up his arms. The natives had thus an opportunity of shooting very many arrows at us. Then we shot four of our guns at them; and although no one was hit, still, the moment they heard the thunderous report, they all fled back to the mountain. There the women, who had killed the youth before our eyes, were now cutting him in pieces, showing us the pieces, roasting them at a large fire which they had made, and eating them. The men, too, made us similar signs, from which we gathered that they had killed our two other Christians in the same manner and had likewise eaten them. And in this respect at least we felt sure that they were speaking the truth.

We were thoroughly maddened by this taunting and by seeing with our own eyes the inhuman way in which they had treated our dead. More than forty of us, therefore, determined to rush to the land and avenge such an inhuman deed and such bestial cruelty. But the commander of our ship would not give his consent; and so, being compelled to endure passively so serious and great an insult, we departed with heavy hearts and with a feeling of great shame, due to the refusal of our captain.

Leaving that land we began to sail between the East and South because the coast line ran in that direction. We made many turns and landings, in the course of which we did not see any tribe which would have any intercourse with us or approach us. We sailed at last so far that we discovered a new land stretching out toward the southwest. Here we rounded a cape (to which we gave the name St. Vincent) and continued our voyage in a southwesterly direction. This Cape St. Vincent is 150 leagues to the southeast of the country where our Christians perished, and eight degrees south of the Equator. As we were sailing along in this manner, one day we noticed on the shore a great number of natives gazing in wonder at us and at the great size of our ships. We anchored in a safe place and then, embarking in our small boats, we reached land. We found the people much kinder than the others; for our toilsome efforts to make them our friends were at last crowned with success. We remained five days among them trading and otherwise dealing with them, and discovered large hollow reed-stalks, most of them still green, and several of them dry on the tops of the trees. We decided to take along with us two of this tribe that they might teach us their tongue; and, indeed, three of them volunteered to return to Portugal with us.

But, since it wearies me to describe all things in detail, may it suffice your Majesty to know that we left that harbor, sailing in a southwesterly direction, keeping always within sight of land, entering many harbors, making frequent landings, and communicating with many tribes. In fact, we sailed so far to the south that we went beyond the Tropic of Capricorn. When we had gone so far south that the South Pole rose thirty-two degrees above the horizon, we lost sight of the Lesser Bear, and the Great Bear itself appeared so low as to be scarcely visible above the horizon. We were then compelled to guide ourselves by the stars of the South Pole, which are far more numerous and much larger and more brilliant than the stars of our Pole. I therefore made a drawing of very many of them, especially of those of the first magnitude, together with the declinations of their orbits around the South Pole, adding also the diameters and semi-diameters of the stars themselves—all of which can be readily seen in my " Four Voyages." In the course of the voyage from Cape St. Augustine, we sailed 700 leagues—100 toward the west and 600 toward the southwest. Should any one desire to describe all that we saw in the course of that voyage, paper would not suffice him. We did not, however, discover anything of great importance with the exception of an infinite number of cassia trees and of very many others which put forth a peculiar kind of leaf. We saw, in addition, very many other wonderful things which it would be tedious to enumerate.

We had now been on our voyage for almost ten months; and, seeing that we discovered no precious metals, we decided to depart thence and to roam over another portion of the sea. As soon as we had come to this conclusion, the word went to each one of our ships that whatever I should think necessary to command in conducting this voyage should be fulfilled to the letter. I therefore immediately gave a general order that all should provide themselves with fuel and water for six months, for the different captains had informed me that their ships could remain at sea only that much longer.

As soon as my orders had been obeyed, we left that coast and began our voyage to the south on the 13th of February, in other words, when the sun was approaching the equinoctial line and returning to this Northern Hemisphere of ours. We sailed so far that the South Pole rose fifty-two degrees above the horizon, and we could no longer see the stars of the Great or the Lesser Bear. For we were then (the 3rd of April) 500 leagues distant from that harbor from which we had begun our southward voyage. On this day so violent a storm arose that we were forced to gather in every stitch of canvas and to run on with bare masts, the southwest wind blowing fiercely and the sea rolling in great billows, in the midst of a furious tempest. The gale was so terrible that all were alarmed in no slight degree. The nights, too, were very long. For on the 7th of April, when the sun was near the end of Aries, we found that the night was fifteen hours long. Indeed, as your Majesty is very well aware, it was the beginning of winter in that latitude. In the midst of this tempest, however, on the 2nd of April, we sighted land, and sailed along shore for nearly twenty leagues. But we found it entirely uninhabited and wild, a land which had neither harbors nor inhabitants. I suppose it was for the reason that it was so cold there that no one could endure such a rigid climate. Furthermore, we found ourselves in such great danger and in the midst of so violent a storm that the different ships could scarcely sight one another. Wherefore the commander of the fleet and I decided that we should signal to all our shipmates to leave that coast, sail out to sea, and make for Portugal.

This plan proved to be a good and necessary one; for, had we remained there one single night longer, we should all have been lost. The day after we left, so great a storm arose that we feared we should be entirely submerged. For this reason we then made many vows to go on pilgrimages and performed other ceremonies, as is customary with sailors. The storm raged round us for five days, during which we could never raise our sails. During the same time we went 250 leagues out to sea, always getting nearer and nearer the equinoctial line, where both sea and sky became more moderate. And here it pleased God on high to deliver us from the above-mentioned dangers. Our course was shaped to the north and northeast, because we desired to make the coast of Ethiopia, from which we were then distant 1,300 leagues, sailing through the Atlantic Ocean. By the grace of God we reached that country on the 10th of May. We rested there for fifteen days upon a stretch of coast facing the south and called Sierra Leone. Then we took our course toward the Azores, which are 750 leagues from Sierra Leone. We reached them about the end of July and again rested for fifteen days. We then set sail for Lisbon, from which we were 300 leagues to the west. And at last, in the year 1502, we again entered the port of Lisbon, in good health as God willed, with only two ships. The third ship we had burned at Sierra Leone, because she was no longer seaworthy.

In this third voyage, we remained at sea for nearly sixteen months, during eleven of which we sailed without being able to see the North Star nor the stars of the Great and the Lesser Bear. At that time we steered by the star of the South Pole.

What I have related above I have deemed the most noteworthy events of my third voyage.

THE FOURTH VOYAGE

I MUST still relate what I saw in my third (sic) voyage. But, in truth, since I have already been tired out by the length of the preceding narratives, and since this voyage did not at all end as I had hoped, on account of an accident that befell us in the Atlantic Ocean, I may be permitted (I trust), to be somewhat brief.

We left Lisbon in six ships with the intention of exploring an island situated toward the horizon and known as Melcha. This island is famous for its wealth, because it is a stopping place for all ships coming from the Gangetic and Indian Seas, precisely as Cadiz is the port for all vessels going from east to west, or in the opposite direction, as is the case with those ships which sail hence for Calicut. This island of Melcha is further to the west than Calicut and more to the south, which we knew from the following fact: that it is situated within sight of the thirty-third degree of the Antarctic Pole.

And so, on the 10th of May, 1503, we set sail from Lisbon (as I have said above), and made for the Cape Verde Islands, where we took on some needed provisions and many other necessary stores. We remained there twelve days, and then set sail with a south wind, because the commander of the fleet, who was haughty and headstrong, issued orders that we should make for Sierra Leone, on the southern coast of Ethiopia. There was no necessity for this, and all of us were unanimously opposed to such a course; but he insisted upon it merely to impress upon us that he had been placed in command of us and the six ships. We made good speed, and just as we were at last coming within sight of our destination, so great and violent a tempest arose, and so heavy a gale began to rage, and Fortune became so unkind, that for four days we could not land in spite of the fact that we could see the coast during the whole of that time. Finally we were obliged to give up our attempts and to continue in what should have been our course from the beginning.

We therefore resumed our voyage with the Suduesius wind blowing (a wind which points between the south and the southwest), and sailed through those difficult seas for 300 leagues. In consequence we went across the Equator by almost three degrees, where land was seen by us twelve leagues off. We were greatly astonished at the sight. It was an island situated in the middle of the sea, very high and remarkable in appearance. It was no larger than two leagues in length by one in width. No man had ever been or lived on that island, and yet it was to us a most unfortunate island. Upon it the commander of our fleet lost his ship, all owing to his own obstinate mind and will. His ship struck upon a rock, sprung leaks, and sank during the night of St. Lawrence, the 10th of August. With the exception of the crew nothing was saved. The ship was of 300 tons, and the strength of our whole fleet lay in her.

While we were all exerting ourselves to see if we could not, perhaps, float her again, the above-mentioned commander ordered me (among other things) to-go in a rowboat to the island in search of a good harbor where we might all draw up our ships in safety. That same commander, however, did not wish me to go with my own ship, because it was m⸱⸱ ⸱d by nine sailors and was then busily engaged ⸱⸱ assisting the endangered ship. He insisted that I go and find such a harbor, where he would restore my ship to me in person. Upon receiving these orders, I went to the island as he desired, taking with me about half the number of my sailors. The island was four leagues away, and hastening thither I discovered a very fine harbor where we might safely anchor our entire fleet. I had now discovered the harbor, and there I spent eight days waiting for the said commander and the rest of our company. I was greatly dis-

turbed when they did not appear, and those who
were with me became so alarmed that they
could not be appeased in any way.

While we were in this state of anxiety, on
the eighth day we saw a ship coming in over
the sea. We at once set out to meet them in
order that they might see us, feeling confident
and at the same time hoping that they would
take us with them to some better harbor. When
we had gotten near and had exchanged greetings, those on board informed us that the commander's ship had been lost at sea, the crew
alone being saved. Your Majesty can readily
imagine the great anxiety which seized me at
this report, when I realized that I was 1,000
leagues distant from Lisbon (to which I must
needs return) in remote and far-off waters.
Nevertheless, we resigned ourselves to the fate
that had come upon us and determined to go on.
First of all we returned to the island, where we
gathered supplies of wood and water for the
ship. The island, indeed, was quite uninhabited and most inhospitable; but it had a great
deal of spring water, countless trees, and numberless land and sea birds, which were so tame
that they permitted us to take them in our
hands. We, therefore, took so many of them
that we entirely filled one of the rowboats.
The only other animals we discovered on that

island were very large mice, lizards with forked tails, and several serpents.

When we had got our provisions on board, we set sail toward the south and southwest; for we had received orders from the King, that, unless some great danger made it impossible, we should follow in the path of our former voyage. Setting out, therefore, in this direction, we at last found a harbor which we called the Bay of All Saints. Indeed, God had granted us such favorable weather that in less than seventeen days we reached this port, which is 300 leagues distant from the above-mentioned island. In the harbor we found neither the commander-in-chief nor any one else of our company, though we waited for them for two months and four days. At the end of this period, seeing that no one arrived there, my companions and I decided to sail further along the coast. After sailing for 260 leagues, we entered a harbor where we determined to build an outpost. Having done so, we left behind in this fort the twenty-four Christians who had been the crew of the luckless ship of our commander-in-chief. We remained in that harbor five months, occupied in constructing the said fort and in loading our ships with brazil-wood. We tarried thus long because our sailors were few in number and because, owing to the lack of many necessary parts, our ships could not proceed further. But when all was done, we agreed to return to Portugal, to do which would require a wind between north and northeast.

We left in the fort the twenty-four Christians, giving them twelve guns and many more arms, and supplying them with provisions to last them six months. During our stay we had made friends with the tribes of that country, of which we have here made very little mention, notwithstanding that we saw great numbers of them and had frequent dealings with them. Indeed, we went about forty leagues into the interior in company with thirty of them. I saw on this expedition very many things which I now pass over in silence, reserving them for my book entitled "The Four Voyages." That country is eight degrees south of the equator and thirty-five degrees west of the meridian of Lisbon, according to our instruments.

We set sail hence with the Nornordensius wind (which is between the north and the northeast) shaping our course for the city of Lisbon. At last, praise be to God, after many hardships and many dangers we entered this harbor of Lisbon in less than seventy-seven days, on the 28th of June, 1504. Here we were received with great honor and with far greater festivities than one would think possible. The reason was that the entire city thought that we had been lost at sea, as was the case with all the rest of our fleet, who had perished owing to the foolish haughtiness of our commander-in-chief. Behold the manner in which God, the just Judge of all, rewards pride!

I am now living at Lisbon, not knowing what next your most serene Majesty will plan for me to do. As for myself, I greatly desire from now on to rest from my many hardships, in the meantime earnestly commending to your Majesty the bearer of the present letter.

AMERIGO VESPUCCI,

in Lisbon.

Greetings from Walter Lud,
Nicholas Lud,
and Martin Ilacomilus

This tome has printed and hereafter oft
Will others print, if Christ our helper be.

The town, St. Deodatus, named for thee
And in the Vosgian Mountains reared aloft.

Finished April 25
MDCVII